A Scholastic Skills Book

A

HOW TO BE A BETTER TEST TAKER

Consultants

Dr. Judith N. Thelen, Professor of Education
Frostburg State College, Frostburg, Maryland

Leonore Itzkowitz, Reading Specialist
Lawrence Intermediate Schools
Trenton, New Jersey

Dr. Stephen Krulik, Professor of Mathematics Education
Temple University, Philadelphia, Pennsylvania

SCHOLASTIC INC.

Editorial, Production, Art Direction

ZIGG-LYN Publishing Concepts and Services, Inc.

Illustrations

Laleine C. Gonzales

ISBN 0-590-35138-9

12 11 10 9 8 7 6 5   7 8 9/9

Printed in the U. S. A.

TABLE OF CONTENTS

LESSON 1 – Getting Ready For A Test

How do you get ready for a test?

(Listen to your teacher.)

ON THE NIGHT BEFORE A TEST:

A student finished studying.

A student is still studying.

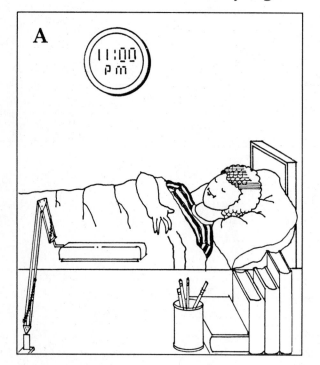 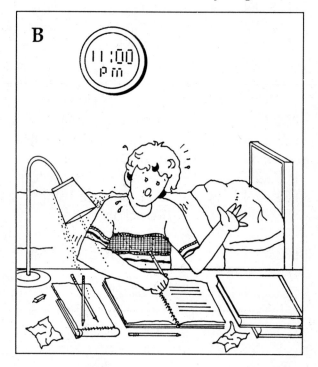

Study the pictures. What do you see in Picture A?
What do you see in Picture B?

(Listen to your teacher.)

Who is ready for a test?
○ The student in Picture A is ready for a test.
○ The student in Picture B is ready for a test.

(Listen to your teacher.)

Check your answer. Did you darken the circle next to the correct answer?

(Listen to your teacher.)

4

ON THE DAY OF TEST:

Students listen, while
teacher tells them what to do.

Students talk, while
teacher tells them what to do.

Students are very nervous.
They do not know what to do.

Students feel good.
They know what to do.

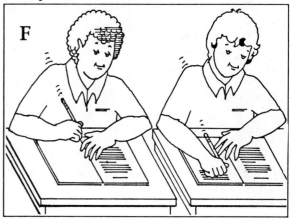

Look at each picture above.

(Listen to your teacher.)

What happens when students listen while the teacher explains?
○ The students are very nervous. They do not know what to do.
○ The students feel good. They know what to do.

(Listen to your teacher.)

Check your answer. Did you darken the circle next to the
correct answer?

(Listen to your teacher.)

5

Do You Know These?
They are signs.
You see them on almost every street.

Many tests use them too.

A test shows the sign: It means **STOP**. Do not go to the next page.	A test shows the sign: It means **GO ON TO THE NEXT PAGE.**

This book uses signs too.

Hi! Call me Ms. BIG EYES.

Hi! I'm HAND an' PENCIL.
Call me HAN'CIL
if you want.

Hello, this is BIG EARS.

We are in this book.
Whenever you see us,
you will ...

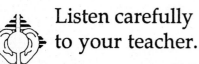 Listen carefully
to your teacher.

 Look carefully.
Be ready
to try a test.

 Be ready
with your
pencil.

What Does a Test Look Like? Your teacher will tell you.(Listen)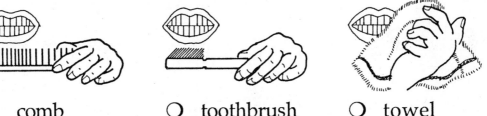

A test has questions and answers.
A question may give three or more answers.
But there is only one correct answer to the question.

 Your teacher will say the test question. Listen carefully.

● dog   ○ cat   ○ monkey

Is the answer right? Your teacher will tell you.   (Listen.)

Your teacher will tell you what to do. Listen.

What do you use to clean your teeth?

○ comb   ○ toothbrush   ○ towel

Is your answer right? Your teacher will tell you.   (Listen.)

✔ **TEST HELP**
When you take a test, remember :
- First, the teacher says the question. Listen carefully.
  If you see the question, read carefully.
- Second, look carefully at the answers with pictures.
- Third, pick the right answer.
- Last, make the circle (○) dark for your answer.

7

How Do You Mark Your Answer?
Your teacher will show and tell you.

(Listen.) 1

Mark an answer in the right place.
Mark an answer in the right way.

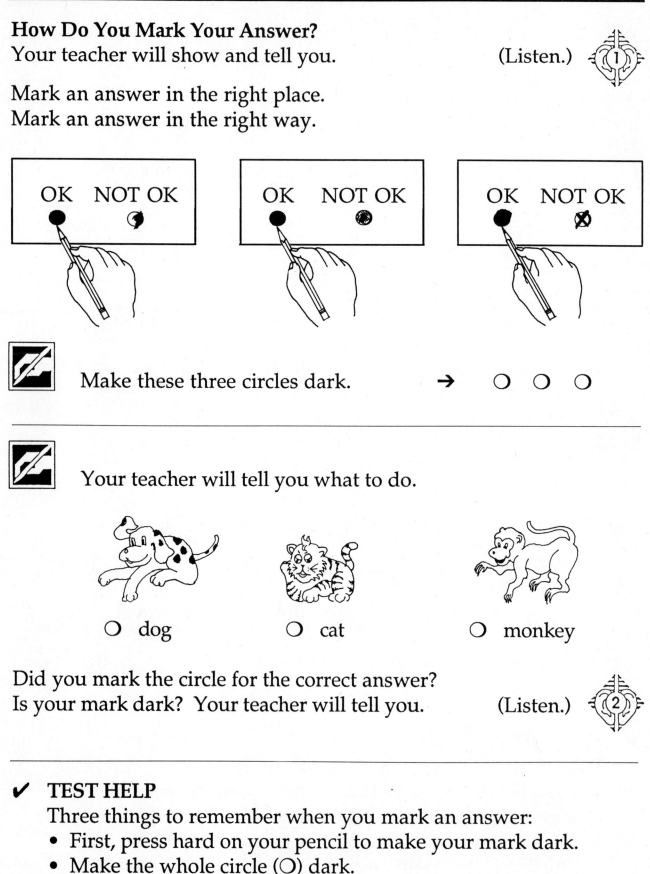

Make these three circles dark. → ○ ○ ○

Your teacher will tell you what to do.

○ dog   ○ cat   ○ monkey

Did you mark the circle for the correct answer?
Is your mark dark? Your teacher will tell you.

(Listen.) 2

✔ **TEST HELP**
Three things to remember when you mark an answer:
- First, press hard on your pencil to make your mark dark.
- Make the whole circle (○) dark.
- Third, don't mark an answer with an ✗.

How Do You Change Your Answer?
Your teacher will tell you.   (Listen.)

This may happen to you:
You make the circle dark for your answer.
You are not sure if your answer is right.
You want to change your answer.
What do you do?

    Your teacher will tell you what to do. Listen.

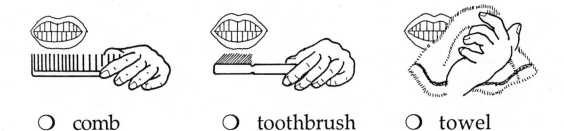

Look at the answer you changed. Is your old mark gone?
Look at your new answer. Is the whole circle dark?

Do it again. Change your answer.

    Your teacher will tell you what to do. Listen.

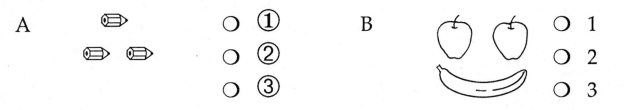

✔ **TEST HELP**

    Two things to remember when you change your answer:

- First, erase your old mark completely.
  Do not cross out the old mark.
- Second, make the whole circle dark for your new answer.

LESSON 2 – Looking at Big and Small Letters

Some tests ask about big and small letters.

How Is The Test Given?   (Your teacher will tell you.)

Look at a test. What do you do in this test?

   Wait. Listen to your teacher.

V →	w ○	b ○	m ○	v ●

Try. Take a test.

   Wait. Listen to your teacher.

M →	m ○	w ○	n ○	h ○

Is your answer right?   (Listen to your teacher.)

✔ **TEST HELP**
Remember:
- Look at the big letter carefully and say its name.
- Then look at each small letter next to it and say its name.
- Mark the circle below the small letter that matches the big letter.

Try these tests.

Your teacher will tell you what to do.

Test 1	C →	a ○	e ○	c ○	o ○
Test 2	J →	j ○	g ○	t ○	k ○
Test 3	E →	c ○	i ○	e ○	r ○
Test 4	B →	h ○	b ○	d ○	l ○
Test 5	I →	r ○	l ○	i ○	t ○
Test 6	G →	g ○	j ○	p ○	z ○
Test 7	H →	b ○	r ○	d ○	h ○
Test 8	Q →	q ○	p ○	j ○	y ○
Test 9	N →	m ○	w ○	u ○	n ○
Test 10	F →	t ○	f ○	k ○	d ○

Are your answers right?   (Listen to your teache

LESSON 3 – Finding the Letter

Some tests ask you to find a letter.

How Is The Test Given?   (Your teacher will tell you.)

Look at a test. What do you do in this test?

 Wait. Listen to your teacher.

S1 →	Zz ○	Aa ○	Xx ●	Bb ○

Try. Take a test.

 Wait. Listen to your teacher.

S2 →	Cc ○	Bb ○	Mm ○	Dd ○

Is your answer right?   (Listen to your teacher.)

✔ **TEST HELP**
Remember:
- Listen carefully to the name of a letter.
- Find the letter among four pairs of letters.
  Name each pair.
- Mark the circle below your answer.

Try these tests.

Your teacher will tell you what to do.

Test **1** →	Tt ○	Ii ○	Hh ○	Ll ○
Test **2** →	Ww ○	Uu ○	Mm ○	Nn ○
Test **3** →	Hh ○	Bb ○	Aa ○	Kk ○
Test **4** →	Kk ○	Ee ○	Ff ○	Rr ○
Test **5** →	Bb ○	Pp ○	Dd ○	Gg ○
Test **6** →	Qq ○	Oo ○	Vv ○	Uu ○
Test **7** →	Yy ○	Vv ○	Aa ○	Gg ○
Test **8** →	Ee ○	Ff ○	Kk ○	Nn ○
Test **9** →	Kk ○	Rr ○	Zz ○	Tt ○
Test **10** →	Ww ○	Nn ○	Mm ○	Uu ○

Are your answers right?   (Listen to your teacher.)

W LESSON 4 – Listening for Beginning Sounds

Which words begin with the same sound?
Some tests ask this question.

How Is The Test Given? (Your teacher will tell you.)

 Wait. Listen for the test word.

Is the answer right? (Listen to your teacher.)

 Wait. Listen for the test word.

Is your answer right? (Listen to your teacher.)

✔ **TEST HELP**
Remember:
- First, listen carefully. The teacher says a test word.
  Listen for the beginning sound.
- Next, name each picture in the test answers.
  Say the name and listen for the beginning sound.
- Pick and mark your answer.

Try these tests.

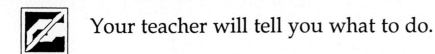 Your teacher will tell you what to do.

Test **1** Wait. Listen for the test word.

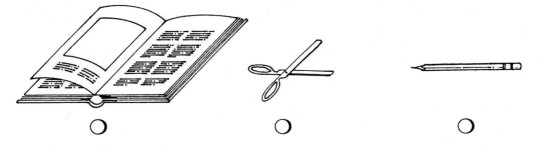

○   ○   ○

Test **2** Wait. Listen for the test word.

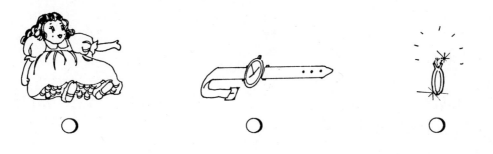

○   ○   ○

Test **3** Wait. Listen for the test word.

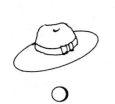

○   ○   ○

Test **4** Wait. Listen for the test word.

○   ○   ○

Are your answers right?   (Listen to your teacher.) 4

15

A test may give the name of a picture.
You will look at the picture and read its name.

What Will The Test Ask You To Do?

 Your teacher will tell you.

Test 1   Wait. Listen for the test word.

sun   bird   tree
○   ○   ○

Is your answer right?   (Listen to your teacher.)   ①

Test 2   Wait. Listen for the test word.

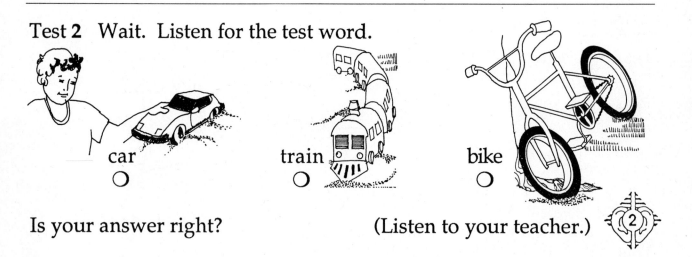

car   train   bike
○   ○   ○

Is your answer right?   (Listen to your teacher.)   ②

✔ **TEST HELP**
Remember:
- First, listen to the teacher say a test word.
  Listen for the beginning sound.
- Next, read the name of each picture.
  Say the name and listen for the beginning sound.
- Pick and mark your answer.

Try these tests.

Your teacher will tell you what to do.

Test **1**   Wait. Listen for the test word.

duck   fish   seal
○   ○   ○

Test **2**   Wait. Listen for the test word.

snake   rabbit   turtle
○   ○   ○

Test **3**   Wait. Listen for the test word.

jacks   kite   top
○   ○   ○

Test **4**   Wait. Listen for the test word.

pig   hen   goat
○   ○   ○

Are your answers right?   (Listen to your teacher.)

LESSON 5 – Listening for End Sounds

You hear a word, and you say a name.
Do they have the same last or end sound?
Some tests ask this question.

How Is The Test Given? (Your teacher will tell you.)

Wait. Listen for the test word.

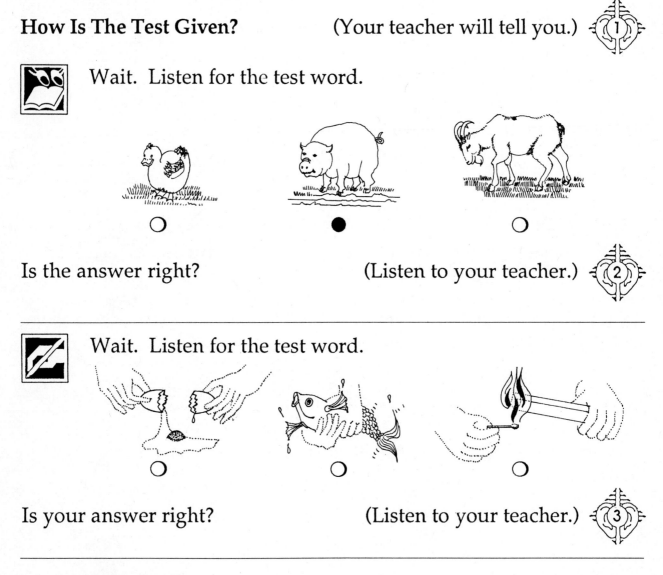

Is the answer right? (Listen to your teacher.)

Wait. Listen for the test word.

Is your answer right? (Listen to your teacher.)

✔ **TEST HELP**
Remember:
- First, listen carefully. The teacher says a test word.
  Listen for the end sound.
- Next, name each picture in the test answers.
  Say the name and listen for the end sound.
- Pick and mark your answer.

Try these tests.

 Your teacher will tell you what to do.

Test **1** Wait. Listen for the test word.

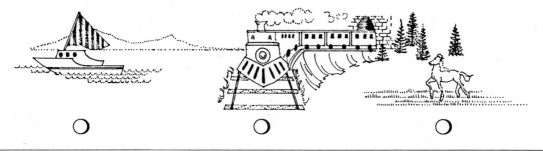

○   ○   ○

Test **2** Wait. Listen for the test word.

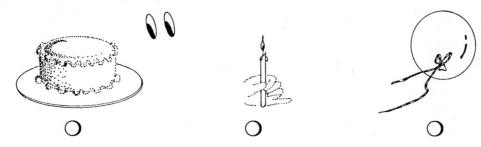

○   ○   ○

Test **3** Wait. Listen for the test word.

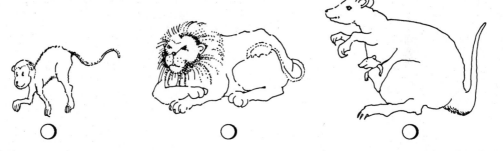

○   ○   ○

Test **4** Wait. Listen for the test word.

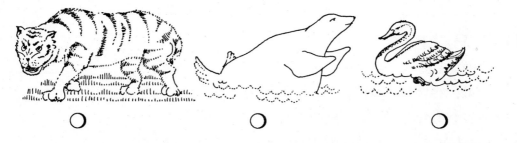

○   ○   ○

Are your answers right?   (Listen to your teacher.) 4

Which words end with the same sound?
Some tests show the names of things in a picture.

How Is the Test Given?   (Your teacher will tell you .)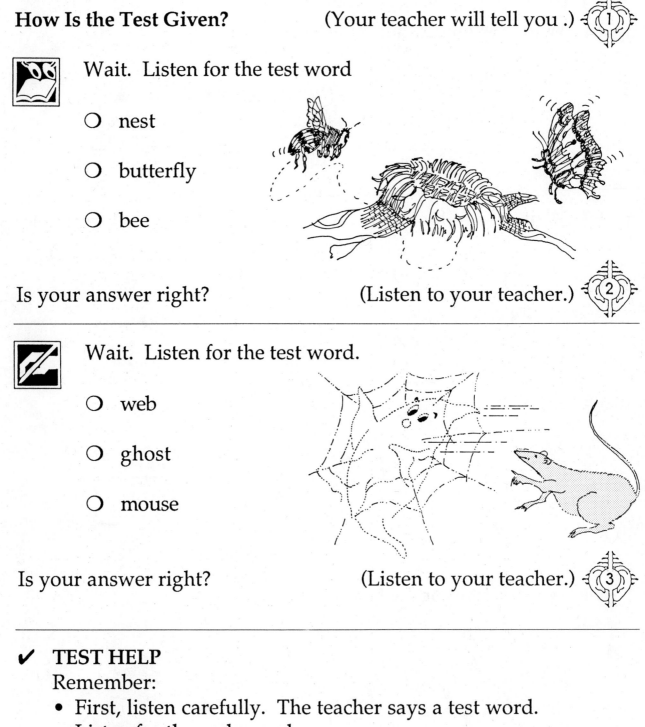

Wait. Listen for the test word

   ○ nest

   ○ butterfly

   ○ bee

Is your answer right?   (Listen to your teacher.)

Wait. Listen for the test word.

   ○ web

   ○ ghost

   ○ mouse

Is your answer right?   (Listen to your teacher.)

✔ **TEST HELP**
Remember:
- First, listen carefully. The teacher says a test word.
  Listen for the end sound.
- Read the given names of things in the picture.
  Listen for the end sound in each name.
- Pick and mark your answer.

Try these tests.

Your teacher will tell you what to do.

Test 1   Wait. Listen for the test word.

- ○ crab
- ○ witch
- ○ bat

Test 2   Wait. Listen for the test word.

- ○ cap
- ○ bat
- ○ ball

Test 3   Wait. Listen for the test word.

- ○ fence
- ○ ladder
- ○ box

Test 4   Wait. Listen for the test word.

- ○ pan
- ○ soap
- ○ fish

Test 5   Wait. Listen for the test word.

- ○ giraffe
- ○ bell
- ○ tree

Are your answers right?   (Listen to your teacher.)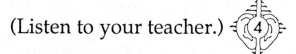

LESSON 6 – Listening for Vowel Sounds

Which words have the same vowel sound?
Some tests ask for the vowel sounds in words.

How Is The Test Given? (Your teacher will tell you.)

Wait. Listen for the test word.

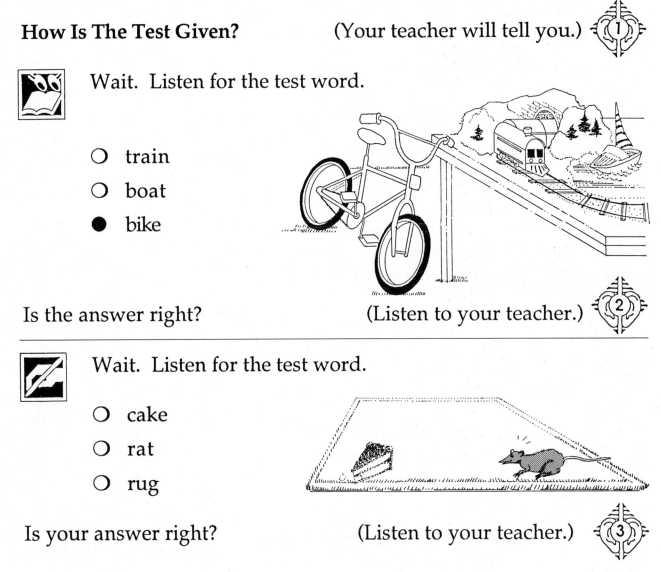

○ train

○ boat

● bike

Is the answer right? (Listen to your teacher.)

Wait. Listen for the test word.

○ cake

○ rat

○ rug

Is your answer right? (Listen to your teacher.)

✔ **TEST HELP**
Remember:
- First, listen carefully to the test word.
  Say it to yourself. Listen to its vowel sound.
- Second, put a finger under a given word.
  Say the word. Listen for its vowel sound.
- Ask: Does it have the same vowel sound as in the test word?
- If yes, mark the circle for that word.

Try these tests.

Your teacher will tell you what to do.

Test **1** Listen for the test word.

wig   dress   hat
○   ○   ○

Test **2** Listen for the test word.

desk   lamp   book
○   ○   ○

Test **3** Listen for the test word.

saw   nails   a x
○   ○   ○

Test **4** Listen for the test word.

wing   jet   kite
○   ○   ○

Test **5** Listen for the test word.

sun   cloud   rose
○   ○   ○

Test **6** Listen for the test word.

shell   seal   bear
○   ○   ○

Test **7** Listen for the test word.

mouse   clock   duck
○   ○   ○

Test **8** Listen for the test word.

fish   deer   bird
○   ○   ○

Are your answers right?   (Listen to your teacher.) 4

W LESSON 7 – Putting Words Together

Which pair of words can make one word?
Some tests ask this question.

How Is The Test Given? (Your teacher will tell you.)

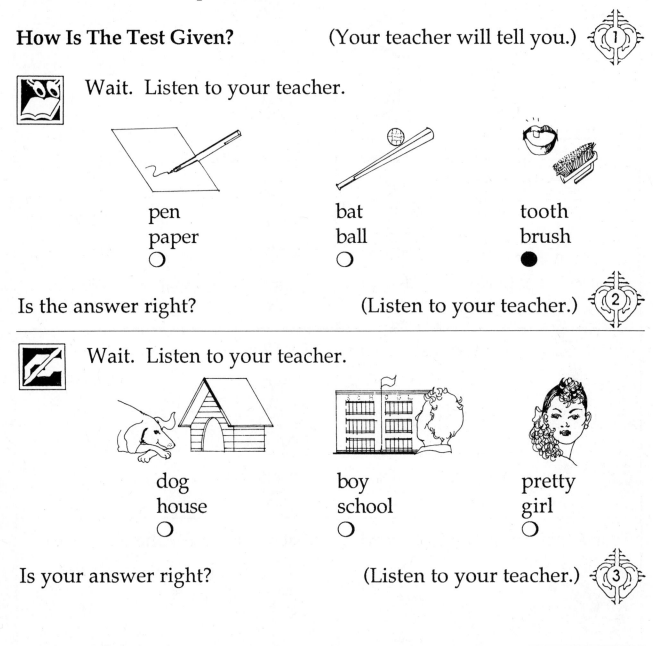

Wait. Listen to your teacher.

pen
paper
○

bat
ball
○

tooth
brush
●

Is the answer right? (Listen to your teacher.)

Wait. Listen to your teacher.

dog
house
○

boy
school
○

pretty
girl
○

Is your answer right? (Listen to your teacher.)

✔ **TEST HELP**
Remember:
  • First, say each pair of words to yourself.
  • Then ask: Which pair can I put together to make a new word?
  • Last, mark the circle below your answer.

24

Try these tests.

Your teacher will tell you what to do.

Test 1	→	big brother ○	grand ma ○	little sister ○
Test 2	→	bread loaf ○	butter fly ○	spider web ○
Test 3	→	front gate ○	open window ○	door knob ○
Test 4	→	old farm ○	cow boy ○	wild horse ○
Test 5	→	pine apple ○	green grapes ○	ripe oranges ○
Test 6	→	cow barn ○	scare crow ○	chicken feed ○
Test 7	→	pair socks ○	five feet ○	shoe lace ○
Test 8	→	bond paper ○	type writer ○	desk lamp ○

Are your answers right?   (Listen to your teacher.)

LESSON 8 – More Practice Tests

What Have You Learned in Lessons 4 to 7?

Listen for Beginning Sounds

Wait. Your teacher will tell you what to do.

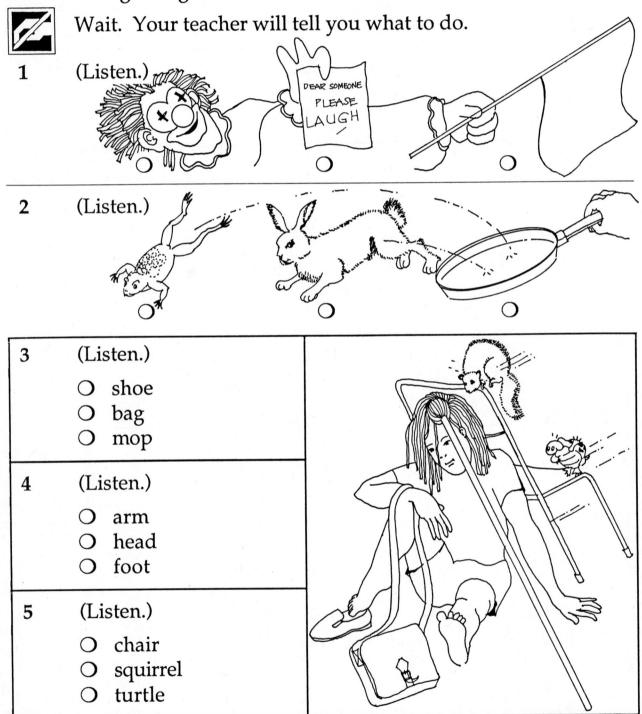

1 (Listen.)

2 (Listen.)

3 (Listen.)
- ○ shoe
- ○ bag
- ○ mop

4 (Listen.)
- ○ arm
- ○ head
- ○ foot

5 (Listen.)
- ○ chair
- ○ squirrel
- ○ turtle

Are your answers right?   (Listen to your teacher.)

More Practice ....

Listen for End Sounds

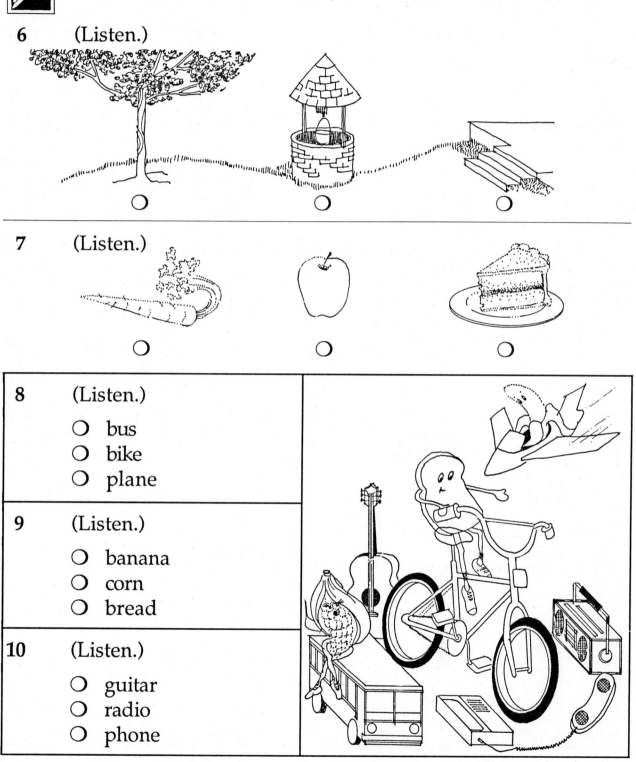

Wait. Your teacher will tell you what to do.

6 (Listen.)

○   ○   ○

7 (Listen.)

○   ○   ○

8 (Listen.)
- ○ bus
- ○ bike
- ○ plane

9 (Listen.)
- ○ banana
- ○ corn
- ○ bread

10 (Listen.)
- ○ guitar
- ○ radio
- ○ phone

Are your answers right?   (Listen to your teacher.)

Listen for Vowel Sounds

Wait. Your teacher will tell you what to do.

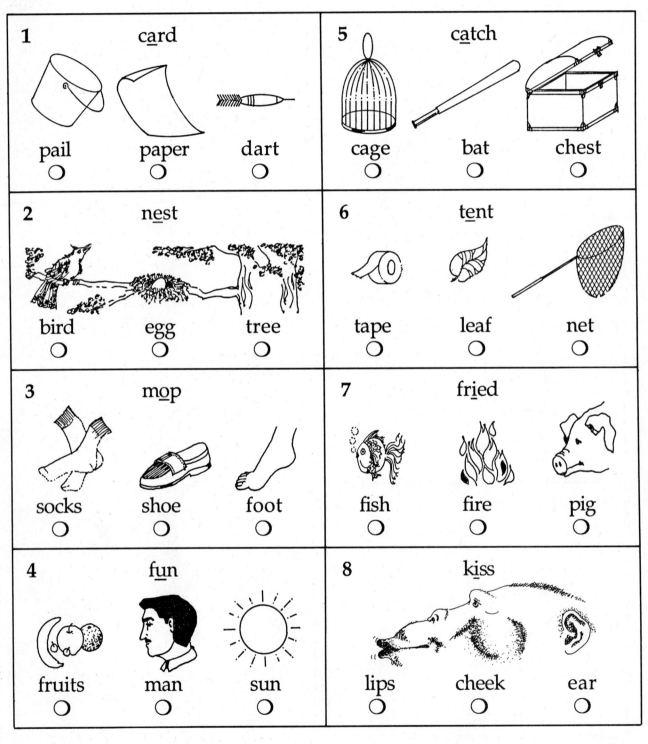

1 card

pail ○   paper ○   dart ○

5 catch

cage ○   bat ○   chest ○

2 nest

bird ○   egg ○   tree ○

6 tent

tape ○   leaf ○   net ○

3 mop

socks ○   shoe ○   foot ○

7 fried

fish ○   fire ○   pig ○

4 fun

fruits ○   man ○   sun ○

8 kiss

lips ○   cheek ○   ear ○

Are your answers right?

(Listen to your teacher.)

Put Words Together

Wait. Your teacher will tell you what to do.

1 →	apple pie ○	some one ○	flower pot ○
2 →	in side ○	love song ○	step up ○
3 →	every thing ○	fast food ○	sad story ○
4 →	cold morning ○	brown paper ○	after noon ○
5 →	secret wish ○	air plane ○	snow white ○
6 →	bus stop ○	play ground ○	eye watch ○
7 →	class room ○	real people ○	noise off ○
8 →	wet paint ○	snake dance ○	home work ○

Are your answers right?   (Listen to your teacher.)

V LESSON 9 – Matching a Picture With a Word

Some tests ask you to match a picture with a word.

How Is The Test Given?   (Your teacher will tell you.) ①

Listen to your teacher.

- ○ kitten

- ○ turtle

- ● bunny

Listen to your teacher.

- ○ walking

- ○ biking

- ○ jumping

Is your answer right?   (Listen to your teacher.) ②

✔ **TEST HELP**
Remember:
- Look at the picture carefully. What is it showing you?
- Then look at each word in the test answers.
  Which word tells what the picture is showing?
- Mark the circle on the left of your answer.

Try these tests.

Your teacher will tell you what to do.

1 (Listen.)

○ grape

○ peach

○ apple

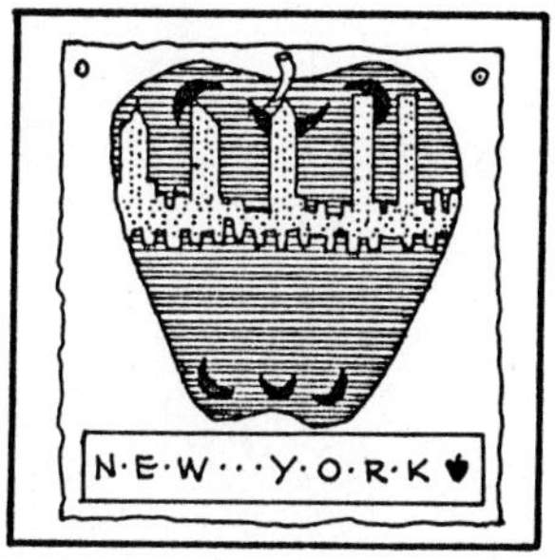

2 (Listen.)

○ spider

○ crab

○ frog

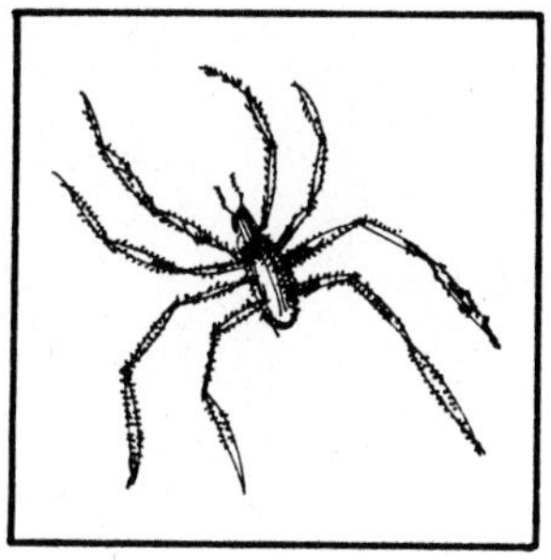

3 (Listen.)

○ clown

○ king

○ ring

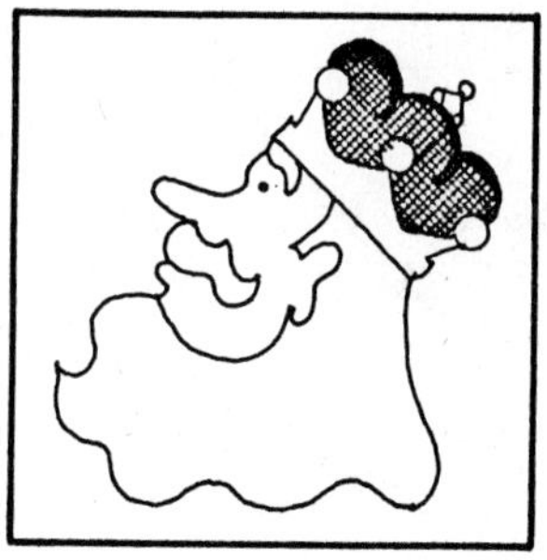

4 (Listen.)

○ vase

○ cup

○ lamp

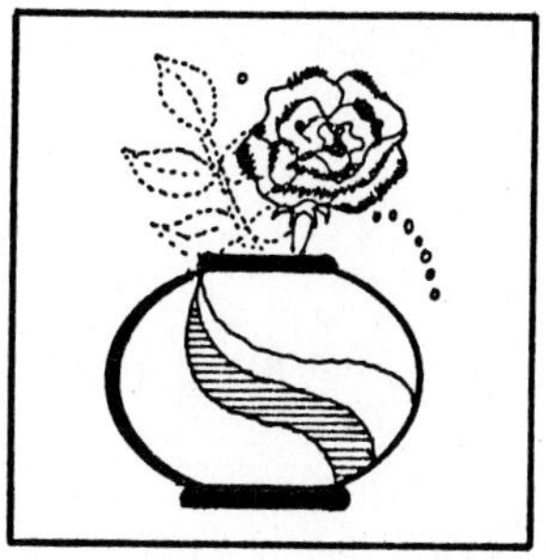

5 (Listen.)

○ playing

○ singing

○ dancing

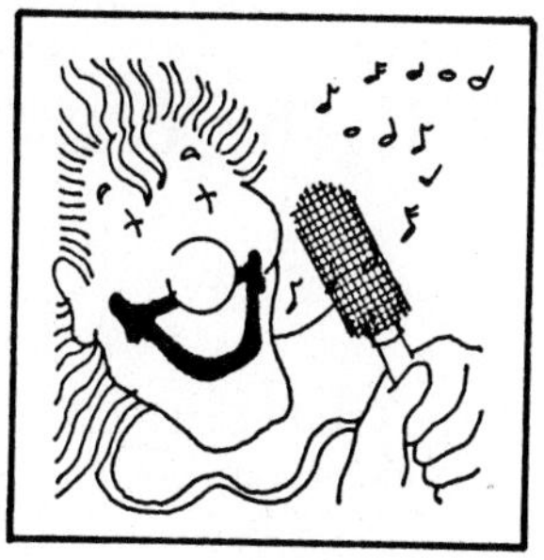

6 (Listen.)

○ eating

○ playing

○ climbing

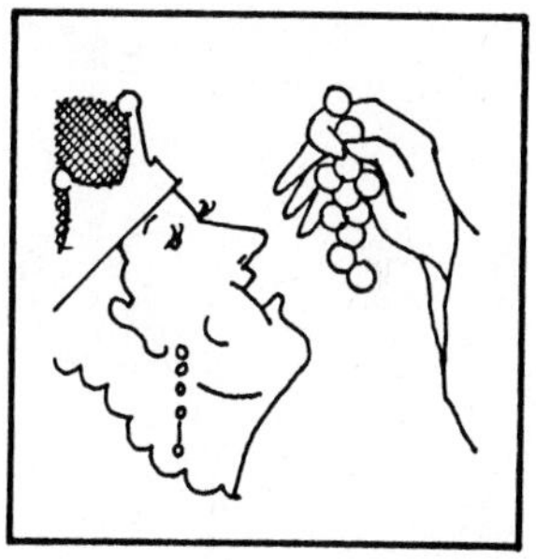

7 (Listen.)

○ bus

○ truck

○ jeep

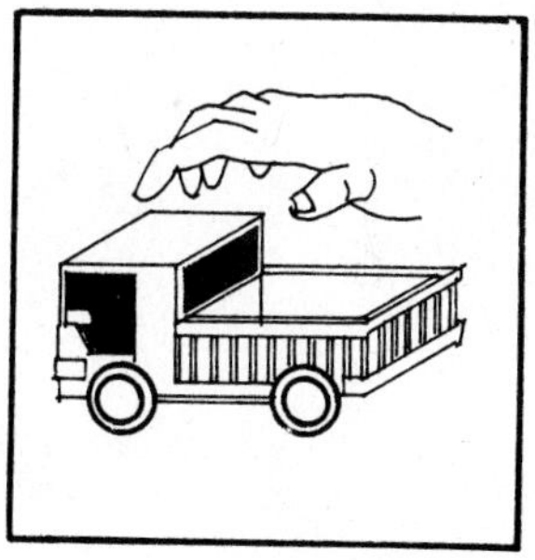

8 (Listen.)

○ resting

○ looking

○ studying

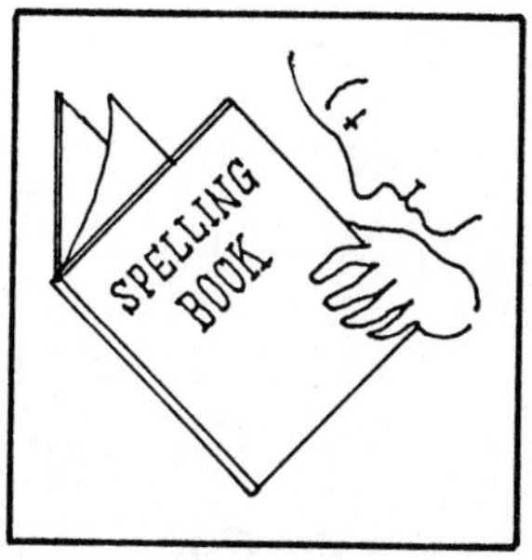

Are your answers right?

(Listen to your teacher.)

LESSON 10 – Listening for Missing Words

Some tests ask, "Which word makes sense in a sentence?"

How Is The Test Given?   (Your teacher will tell you.) ①

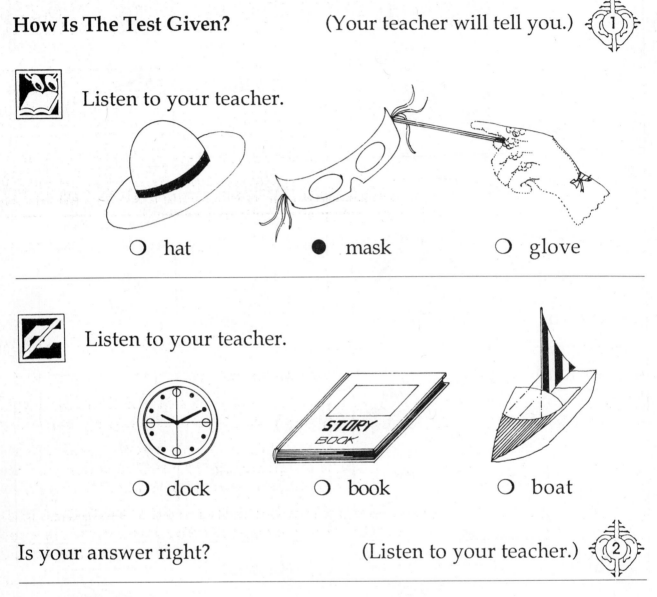

Listen to your teacher.

○ hat   ● mask   ○ glove

Listen to your teacher.

○ clock   ○ book   ○ boat

Is your answer right?   (Listen to your teacher.) ②

✔ **TEST HELP**
Remember:
- First, listen carefully to the sentence with the missing word.
  Say the sentence to yourself.
  Try each answer word in the blank.
- Ask yourself, "Which word makes sense in the sentence?"
- Then mark the circle near the answer word that makes the most sense.

Try these tests.

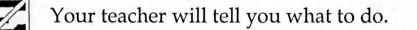

Your teacher will tell you what to do.

1 (Listen.)

- ○ moon
- ○ calendar
- ○ map

5 (Listen.)

- ○ socks
- ○ shoes
- ○ scissors

2 (Listen.)

- ○ eater
- ○ nurse
- ○ cook

6 (Listen.)

- ○ brave
- ○ pretty
- ○ poor

3 (Listen.)

- ○ tail
- ○ head
- ○ ears

7 (Listen.)

- ○ shout
- ○ break
- ○ burn

4 (Listen.)

- ○ face
- ○ nose
- ○ eyes

8 (Listen.)

- ○ singer
- ○ clown
- ○ dancer

Are your answers right?   (Listen to your teacher.)

LESSON 11 – Reading for Missing Words

Some tests show the sentences with missing words.

How Is The Test Given?   (Your teacher will tell you.)

Look at a test. What do you do in this test?

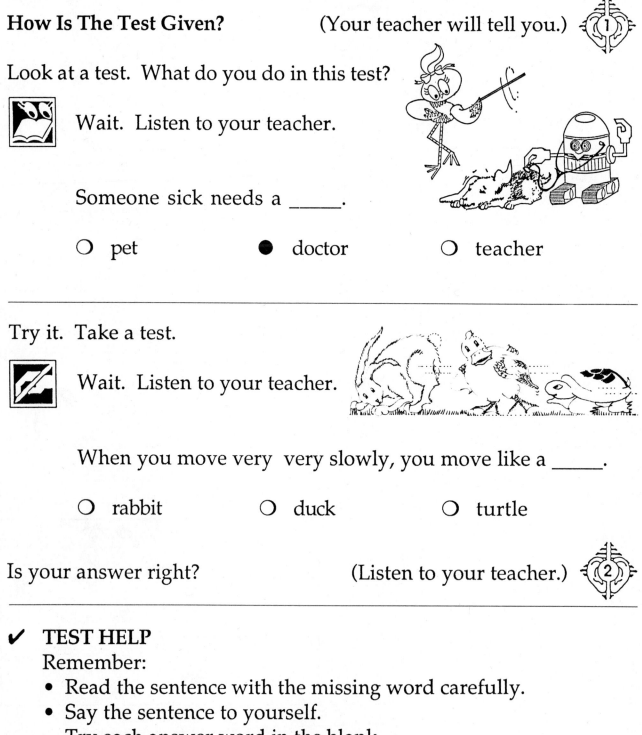

Wait. Listen to your teacher.

Someone sick needs a _____.

○ pet   ● doctor   ○ teacher

Try it. Take a test.

Wait. Listen to your teacher.

When you move very very slowly, you move like a _____.

○ rabbit   ○ duck   ○ turtle

Is your answer right?   (Listen to your teacher.)

✔ **TEST HELP**
Remember:
- Read the sentence with the missing word carefully.
- Say the sentence to yourself.
  Try each answer word in the blank.
- Ask yourself, "Which word makes sense in the sentence?"
- Mark the circle that is near your answer.

Try these tests.

Your teacher will tell you what to do.

1	You pound a nail on the wall with a _____. ○ dart ○ hammer ○ saw
2	When you eat, you use a knife and a _____. ○ straw ○ fork ○ finger
3	Pictures are taken with a _____. ○ pencil ○ frame ○ camera
4	You go to bed when you are _____. ○ hungry ○ sad ○ sleepy
5	Seashells are found on the _____. ○ bridge ○ beach ○ tree
6	The sound made by a lion is a _____. ○ roar ○ moo ○ bark
7	Something funny can make you _____. ○ cry ○ laugh ○ angry
8	When you feel bad about a mistake, you feel _____. ○ sorry ○ right ○ happy

Are your answers right?   (Listen.) 3

LESSON 12 – More Practice Tests

What Have You Learned in Lessons 9 to 11?

Match a Picture With the Right Word

Your teacher will tell you what to do.

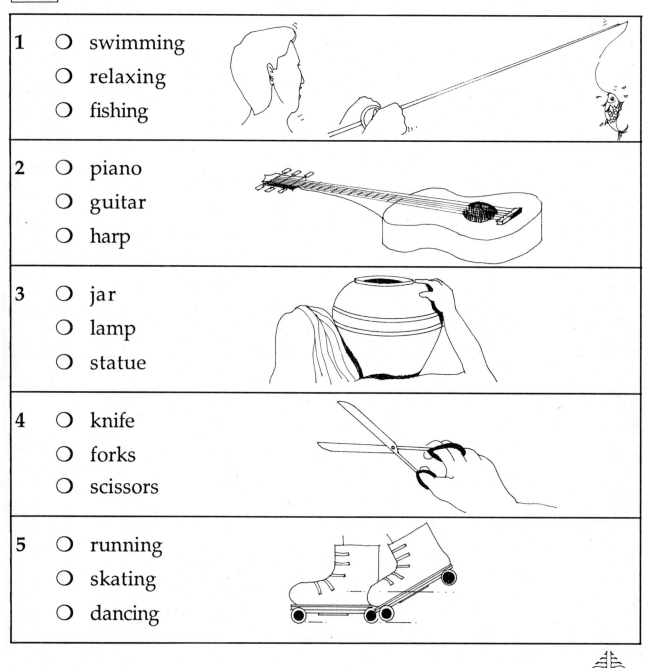

1 ○ swimming
　○ relaxing
　○ fishing

2 ○ piano
　○ guitar
　○ harp

3 ○ jar
　○ lamp
　○ statue

4 ○ knife
　○ forks
　○ scissors

5 ○ running
　○ skating
　○ dancing

Are your answers right?　　　　　　(Listen.) ◁ 1

More Practice ....

Listen to Sentences With Missing Words

Your teacher will tell you what to do.

6 (Listen.)
- ○ tie
- ○ shirt
- ○ hat

10 (Listen.)
- ○ dirty
- ○ black
- ○ empty

7 (Listen.)
- ○ morning
- ○ noon
- ○ evening

11 (Listen.)
- ○ laugh
- ○ play
- ○ eat

8 (Listen.)
- ○ toys
- ○ pets
- ○ prizes

12 (Listen.)
- ○ grow
- ○ learn
- ○ listen

9 (Listen.)
- ○ frowning
- ○ smiling
- ○ speaking

13 (Listen.)
- ○ neighbors
- ○ toys
- ○ friends

Are your answers right?

(Listen.) ②

Read Sentences With Missing Words

Your teacher will tell you what to do.

---

1 Sugar tastes _____.

  ○ sweet   ○ sour   ○ salty

---

2 When you are brave you are not _____.

  ○ weak   ○ smart   ○ afraid

---

3 The day you were born is your _____.

  ○ age   ○ party   ○ birthday

---

4 When you help others, you are _____.

  ○ bad   ○ bright   ○ kind

---

5 To be number one is to be _____.

  ○ better   ○ first   ○ perfect

---

6 Your pet can be your best _____.

  ○ friend   ○ flower   ○ picture

Are your answers right?   (Listen.)

R LESSON 13 – Telling About Pictures

A test may ask you to tell what you see in a picture.

How Is The Test Given?   (Your teacher will tell you.) ⟨1⟩

Look at a test. What do you do in this test?

Wait. Listen to your teacher.

Melissa is blowing the _____ on her birthday cake.

- ○ icing
- ○ balloons
- ● candles

Try. Take a test.

Wait. Listen to your teacher.

Melissa is _____ years old.

- ○ five
- ○ six
- ○ seven

Is your answer right?   (Listen.) ⟨2⟩

✔ **TEST HELP**
Remember:
- Look at the picture carefully.
  You must look at everything in the picture.
- Then read the sentence with the missing word.
  Figure out what the sentence is saying about the picture.
  Say each answer word in the sentence.
- Pick the word which makes the sentence tell about the picture.
- Mark the circle beside your answer.

39

R Try these tests.

Your teacher will tell you what to do.

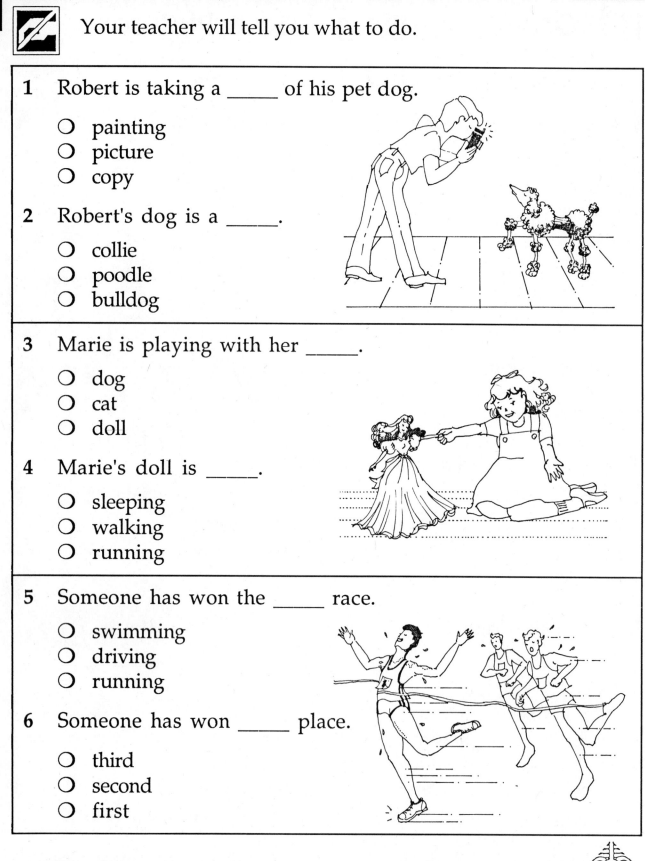

1 Robert is taking a _____ of his pet dog.

- ○ painting
- ○ picture
- ○ copy

2 Robert's dog is a _____.

- ○ collie
- ○ poodle
- ○ bulldog

3 Marie is playing with her _____.

- ○ dog
- ○ cat
- ○ doll

4 Marie's doll is _____.

- ○ sleeping
- ○ walking
- ○ running

5 Someone has won the _____ race.

- ○ swimming
- ○ driving
- ○ running

6 Someone has won _____ place.

- ○ third
- ○ second
- ○ first

Are your answers right?   (Listen to your teacher.)   3

LESSON 14 – Reading for Things You Know

A test may ask about things you know.
It may ask if something is true or not true.

How Is The Test Given?   (Your teacher will tell you.) ⊰①⊱

Look at a test. What do you do in this test?

Wait. Listen to your teacher.

Can monkeys sing?

○ Yes   ● No

Try. Take a test.

Wait. Listen to your teacher.

Are clowns funny-looking?

○ Yes   ○ No

Is your answer right?   (Listen to your teacher.) ⊰②⊱

✔ **TEST HELP**
Remember:
- Be sure to read the test question carefully.
  Think about what the question is about. Is it true or not?
- Then mark the circle beside your answer.

R

Try these tests.

Your teacher will tell you what to do.

1   Can a cat moo?
   ○ Yes   ○ No

2   Do doctors get sick?
   ○ Yes   ○ No

3   Can a doll tell a lie?
   ○ Yes   ○ No

4   Can a clock tell time?
   ○ Yes   ○ No

5   Does the sun shine at night?
   ○ Yes   ○ No

6   Can a squirrel climb a tree?
   ○ Yes   ○ No

7   Can a kitten become a cat?
   ○ Yes   ○ No

8   Does a wall have ears?
   ○ Yes   ○ No

9   Do elephants have trunks?
   ○ Yes   ○ No

10 Can a corn ear hear?
   ○ Yes   ○ No

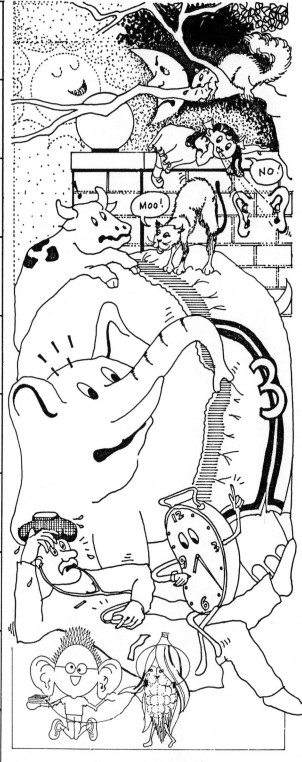

Are your answers right?

(Listen to your teacher.)

R

LESSON 15 – Reading a Story

Some tests ask questions about a story.

How Is The Test Given?   (Your teacher will tell you.)

 Look at a test. What do you do in this test?

Martha was giving her dog Benjie
a bath. Benjie will be in a dog show
in an hour.

A cat passed by. Benjie ran after
the cat.

When Benjie came back, he was black
all over with mud.

"Forget the dog show," Martha said.

 Wait.

1   What was Martha doing?

- ○ She's playing with her dog.
- ○ She's teaching her dog.
- ● She's giving her dog a bath.

Are your answers right?

Wait.

2   What did Benjie do when he saw a cat?

- ○ Benjie barked at the cat.
- ○ Benjie ran away.
- ○ Benjie ran after the cat.

(Listen to your teacher.)

✔ **TEST HELP**
Remember:
- Listen to the story carefully. Read each sentence in the story. Understand what the story is about.
- Read the test question and the different answers. Look for the sentence in the story that answers the question.
- Pick your answer and mark the circle beside it.

Your teacher will tell you what to do.

The monkey and the turtle once hated each other. One day the monkey caught the turtle.

The monkey said, "I'll burn you alive!"

"That's nice," said the turtle, smiling. "Now I can get warm."

"Maybe it's better to throw you down the cliff," the monkey said.

"Do what you want," the turtle said. "But please, don't throw me into the sea!" he begged.

The monkey threw the turtle into the sea.

"Thank you," the turtle shouted, laughing, and swam away.

---

1 What did the monkey want first?
- ○ The monkey wanted to throw the turtle down the cliff.
- ○ The monkey wanted to throw the turtle into the fire.
- ○ The monkey wanted to throw the turtle into the sea.

Is your answer right? (Listen to your teacher.)

---

2 What did the monkey finally do with the turtle?
- ○ The monkey burned the turtle alive.
- ○ The monkey threw the turtle down the cliff.
- ○ The monkey threw the turtle into the sea

Is your answer right? (Listen to your teacher.)

---

3 Why did the turtle laugh at the end of the story?
- ○ He tricked the monkey.
- ○ He loved swimming.
- ○ He hated the monkey.

Is your answer right? (Listen to your teacher.)

R LESSON 16 – Reading About True Things

Some tests want you to find something true in a story.

How Is The Test Given?   (Your teacher will tell you.)

Look at a test. What do you do in this test?

How are turtles born?
First the mother turtle lays eggs in the sand.
Next, she covers the eggs to keep them warm.
Then the eggs hatch. The baby turtles begin
to crawl out of the shell.

Wait.   Wait.

1   You can find turtle eggs   2   First, baby turtles
     in the _____.   are _____.

     ○ sea   ○ eggs
     ○ rocks   ○ shells
     ● sand   ○ fish

Are your answers right?   (Listen to your teacher.)

✔ **TEST HELP**
Remember:
- Always listen carefully as the teacher reads the story.
- Read each sentence in the story.
  Understand what the sentences are saying.
- Next read the test sentence with a missing part.
  Read the test answers.
- Look at the story sentences again.
  Then pick and mark your answer.

Your teacher will tell you what to do.

There are tiny drops of water in the clouds.
During winter, these drops get very cold.
They turn into snowflakes and fall to the ground.

1 The word used in the story that means very small is _____.

○ there   ○ tiny   ○ turn

2 At first, snowflakes are tiny drops of _____.

○ water   ○ snow   ○ cold

3 Drops of water get very cold during _____.

○ fall   ○ winter   ○ cloudy

4 When tiny drops of water get very cold, they become _____.

○ clouds   ○ rain   ○ snowflakes

Are your answers right?   (Listen to your teacher.)

R LESSON 17 – More Practice Tests

What Have You Learned in Lessons 13 to 16?

Tell About Pictures

Your teacher will tell you what to do.

1 Marco is playing with his toy _____.
- ○ trains
- ○ trucks
- ○ planes

2 He has _____ toy trucks.
- ○ two
- ○ three
- ○ four

3 Lisa is learning how to play the _____.
- ○ guitar
- ○ flute
- ○ piano

4 Her _____ is watching her.
- ○ brother
- ○ teacher
- ○ mother

5 Tom is flying a _____.
- ○ plane
- ○ rocket
- ○ kite

6 There is a strong wind _____.
- ○ blowing
- ○ running
- ○ shining

Are your answers right?   (Listen to your teacher.)

Is It True?

 Your teacher will tell you what to do.

1	**Are all dogs friendly?** ○ Yes ○ No
2	**Can a dog swim?** ○ Yes ○ No
3	**Can teeth clean a toothbrush?** ○ Yes ○ No
4	**Can teeth chew food?** ○ Yes ○ No
5	**Can the wind blow your hat away?** ○ Yes ○ No
6	**Can you see the wind?** ○ Yes ○ No

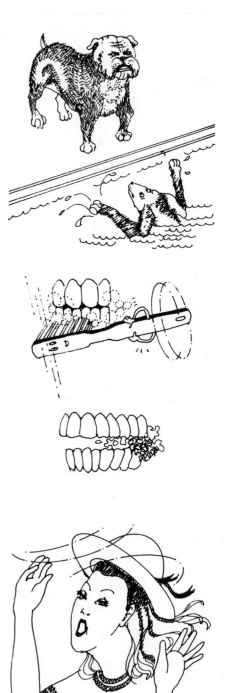

Are your answers right?   (Listen to your teacher.)

More Practice ....

What is Happening in the Story?

 Your teacher will tell you what to do.

Paul and Jenny saw a horror movie. They pretended not to be scared.

On their way home, they saw a pair of green eyes shining in the dark.

"It's the green-eyed monster!" Jenny cried out.

Paul picked up a stone and threw it at the pair of green eyes.

The eyes were gone. They heard the monster running away, crying, "Meow! Meow!"

1 Which word tells about a horror movie?

○ funny   ○ sad   ○ scary

2 What did Jenny think she saw in the dark?

○ dog   ○ monster   ○ owl

3 What did Paul throw at the pair of green eyes?

○ a ball   ○ a stick   ○ a stone

4 What did the monster turn out to be?

○ a cat   ○ a ghost   ○ a boy

Are your answers right?   (Listen to your teacher.)

Find Something True in a Story

Your teacher will tell you what to do.

> Why does cuckoo also mean crazy or foolish?
>
> The cuckoo bird has strange habits. It does not build its own nest.
>
> Instead, it lays its eggs in another bird's nest. The cuckoo lays one egg in each nest that it finds.
>
> The other bird hatches the cuckoo's egg. It takes care of the baby cuckoo like its own. It feeds and cares for the baby cuckoo.
>
> Then the baby cuckoo learns to fly. It flies away and joins other cuckoos.

1   A mother cuckoo does not build its own _____ .

    ◯ hatch   ◯ nest   ◯ egg

2   A cuckoo lays its eggs in a nest built by another _____ .

    ◯ cuckoo   ◯ man   ◯ bird

3   Another bird feeds and cares for the cuckoo's _____ .

    ◯ baby   ◯ nest   ◯ egg

4   When the baby cuckoo learns to fly, it joins other _____ .

    ◯ sparrows   ◯ robins   ◯ cuckoos

Are your answers right?   (Listen to your teacher.)

LESSON 18 – Spelling

Is the name or word spelled right?
Some tests may ask this question.

How Is The Test Given?   (Your teacher will tell you.)

Look at a test. What do you do in this test?

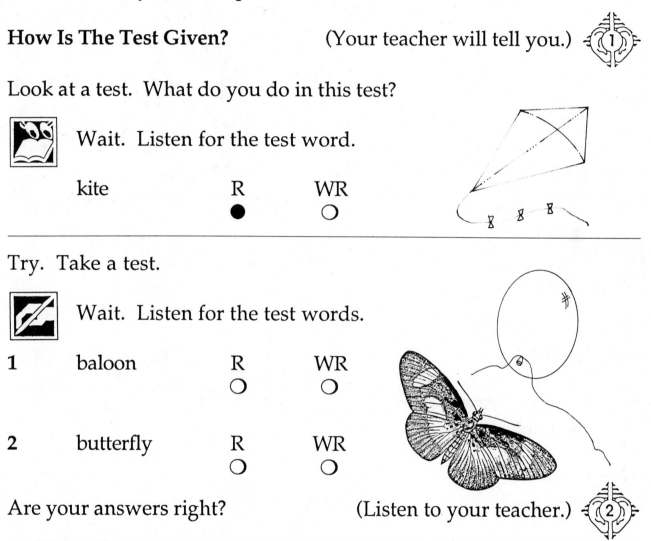

Wait. Listen for the test word.

kite   R   WR
            ●   ○

Try. Take a test.

Wait. Listen for the test words.

1   baloon   R   WR
                   ○   ○

2   butterfly   R   WR
                   ○   ○

Are your answers right?   (Listen to your teacher.)

✔ **TEST HELP**
Remember:
- Listen carefully as the teacher says the test word.
  Listen for the sounds in the test word.
- Then look at the picture and its name.
  Is the name of the picture spelled right?
- If the name is spelled right, mark the circle below **R**, for *Right*.
  If the name is not spelled right, mark the circle below **WR**,
  for *Wrong*.

Is the name or word spelled right?

Your teacher will tell you what to do.

1	carot	R ◯	WR ◯
2	rabit	R ◯	WR ◯
3	cou	R ◯	WR ◯
4	hay	R ◯	WR ◯
5	shep	R ◯	WR ◯
6	farmer	R ◯	WR ◯
7	pumpken	R ◯	WR ◯
8	tructor	R ◯	WR ◯
9	korn	R ◯	WR ◯
10	chickeen	R ◯	WR ◯

Are your answers right?

(Listen to your teacher.) ⊰3⊱

LESSON 19 – Finding the Right Spelling

In some tests, you must pick the right spelling of a word.

How Is The Test Given? (Your teacher will tell you.)

Look at a test. What do you do in this test?

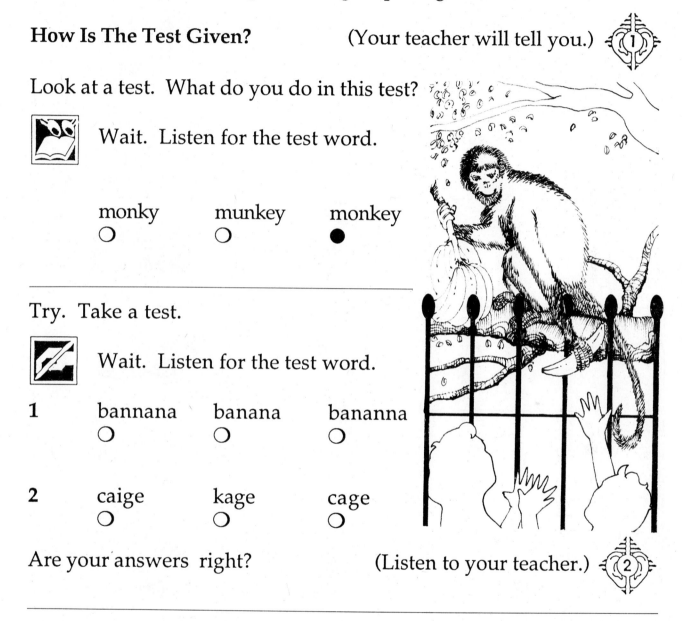

Wait. Listen for the test word.

monky   munkey   monkey
○   ○   ●

Try. Take a test.

Wait. Listen for the test word.

1   bannana   banana   bananna
    ○   ○   ○

2   caige   kage   cage
    ○   ○   ○

Are your answers right?   (Listen to your teacher.)

✔ **TEST HELP**
Remember:
- Listen carefully as the teacher says the test word.
  Look at the picture. It shows what the word stands for.
- Look at the different spellings of the word.
  Which spelling has all the correct letters of the word?
- Mark the circle below your answer.

Which is the right spelling?

Your teacher will tell you what to do.

1	hous ○	house ○	haus ○	
2	byke ○	bike ○	baik ○	
3	stor ○	stour ○	store ○	
4	moni ○	mony ○	money ○	
5	flower ○	flawer ○	flowr ○	
6	putato ○	potato ○	potaeto ○	
7	hungri ○	hangri ○	hungry ○	

Are your answers right?   (Listen to your teacher.)

54

LESSON 20 – Using Capital Letters

Which word needs a big or capital letter?
Some tests ask you this question.

How Is The Test Given?   (Your teacher will tell you.)

Look at a test. What do you do in this test?

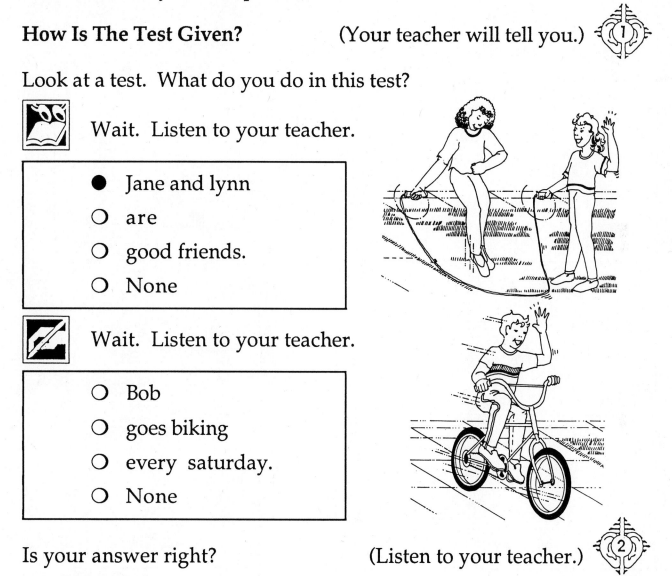

Wait. Listen to your teacher.

- ● Jane and lynn
- ○ are
- ○ good friends.
- ○ None

Wait. Listen to your teacher.

- ○ Bob
- ○ goes biking
- ○ every saturday.
- ○ None

Is your answer right?   (Listen to your teacher.)

✔ **TEST HELP**
Remember:
- Look at each part of the test sentence carefully.
- Is there a word that needs a capital letter?
- Mark the circle beside the part where that word is found.
  If there is no word that needs a capital letter, mark the circle beside **None**.

55

Is there a word that needs a capital letter?

 Your teacher will tell you what to do.

1	○ Miss perez
	○ teaches
	○ Spanish.
	○ None
2	○ The pandas
	○ came
	○ from china.
	○ None
3	○ the Australian twins
	○ Mark and Paul wear
	○ name tags in class.
	○ None
4	○ Danny's grandfather
	○ came from
	○ New Delhi, india.
	○ None
5	○ Jim and his family
	○ visited Mt. Rushmore
	○ in South Dakota.
	○ None

Are your answers right?

(Listen to your teacher.)

LESSON 21 – Using End Marks

Which of these end marks will you use? $\boxed{.}$ $\boxed{?}$ $\boxed{!}$

Some tests ask for the right mark to use at the end of a sentence.

How Is The Test Given?   (Your teacher will tell you.)

Look at a test. What do you do in this test?

Wait. Listen to your teacher.

Mike woke up early in the morning
● .   ○ ?   ○ !   ○ None

Try. Take a test.

Wait. Listen to your teacher.

1   Who was the first man to walk on the moon
○ .   ○ ?   ○ !   ○ None

2   Ronald loves his toy rocket ship.
○ .   ○ ?   ○ !   ○ None

Are your answers right?   (Listen to your teacher.)

✔ **TEST HELP**
Remember:
- Look for the mark at the end of the test sentence.
  Look for a period (.), a question mark (?), or a surprise or wow mark (!).
- If there is an end mark, you don't need one.
  Mark the circle beside None.
- If there is no end mark, pick one. a (.), a (?), or a (!)
- Mark the circle beside the mark you picked.

Which end mark will you use?

Your teacher will tell you what to do.

1 What's your favorite dog?
   ○ .   ○ ?   ○ !   ○ None

2 The poodle came from Germany
   ○ .   ○ ?   ○ !   ○ None

3 Now there are more poodles in France.
   ○ .   ○ ?   ○ !   ○ None

4 The greyhound runs very fast
   ○ .   ○ ?   ○ !   ○ None

5 That is why a bus company uses that name
   ○ .   ○ ?   ○ !   ○ None

6 What a big dog
   ○ .   ○ ?   ○ !   ○ None

7 It's a bulldog
   ○ .   ○ ?   ○ !   ○ None

8 Did the first bulldog come from England
   ○ .   ○ ?   ○ !   ○ None

9 St. Bernards save people in snowy mountains
   ○ .   ○ ?   ○ !   ○ None

10 What a great dog
   ○ .   ○ ?   ○ !   ○ None

Are your answers right?   (Listen to your teacher.)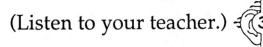

LESSON 22 – Picking the Best Sentence

Which is the best sentence?
A test may ask this question.

How Is The Test Given?   (Your teacher will tell you.)

     Wait. Listen to your teacher.

- ○ Miss Chan she our math teacher.

- ● She can add big numbers.

- ○ I wishing I could do that, too.

Wait. Listen to your teacher.

- ○ Mr. Gray finding books very fast.

- ○ Him is working in the library.

- ○ He helps me look for books.

Is your answer right?   (Listen to your teacher.)

✔ **TEST HELP**
Remember:
- Read each sentence carefully.
- Pick the only correct sentence among the three sentences.
- Mark the circle beside your answer.

Which is the best sentence?

Your teacher will tell you what to do.

1 ○ Sam is me friend.
   ○ He lives next door.
   ○ I play and Sam all the time.

2 ○ I seen Sam's father yesterday.
   ○ He done looked at my tonsils.
   ○ Sam's father is a doctor.

3 ○ Sarah done what dentist say.
   ○ She brush teeth every day.
   ○ She has pretty teeth.

4 ○ Dad's car was all broke down.
   ○ He brung it to the shop.
   ○ The car was fixed.

5 ○ Mom sent me to the bakery.
   ○ To the baker we gone.
   ○ Hot and fresh is the bread .

6 ○ Don't fish can sleep?
   ○ Fish eyes don't close.
   ○ Fish do takes naps.

7 ○ The aardvark is a strange animal.
   ○ It have ears like donkey-ears.
   ○ It have mouth like pig.

8 ○ Some birds flying ten hours.
   ○ They don't get tired.
   ○ They're body is strong.

9 ○ Animals talks to other animals.
   ○ Animals talking by smell.
   ○ They also talk by sounds.

10 ○ Sharks are sharp teeth.
   ○ Sharks' old tooth will fall.
   ○ New tooth will grows.

Are your answers right?

(Listen to your teacher.)

LESSON 23 – More Practice Tests

What Have You Learned in Lessons 18 to 22?

Spelling

Wait. Your teacher will tell you what to do.

1	(Listen.)			
	cookie ○	cooky ○	cooki ○	

2	(Listen.)			
	flog ○	frog ○	frag ○	

3	(Listen.)			
	brid ○	berd ○	bird ○	

4	(Listen.)			
	horse ○	hors ○	hose ○	

5	(Listen.)			
	char ○	tsayr ○	chair ○	

Are your answers right?   (Listen to your teacher.)

Capital Letters and End Marks

Wait. Your teacher will tell you what to do.

1	Jack and jill		are going up		the hill.	None
	○		○		○	○

2	They want to see		the california Angels		play.	None
	○		○		○	○

3	the top	of the hill		was too far.	None
	○	○		○	○

4	Toronto Blue Jays		won	the game.	None
	○		○	○	○

5	Jill and Jack		are still going		up the hill.	None
	○		○		○	○

Are your answers right?   (Listen to your teacher.) ①

Wait. Your teacher will tell you what to do.

6	Do you stop, look, and listen before crossing the street
	○ . ○ ? ○ ! ○ None

7	Stop when the light is red
	○ . ○ ? ○ ! ○ None

8	Wait until the light turns green
	○ . ○ ? ○ ! ○ None

9	Do you look to your left and then to your right
	○ . ○ ? ○ ! ○ None

10	A car is coming. Look out
	○ . ○ ? ○ ! ○ None

Are your answers right?   (Listen to your teacher.) ②

Pick the Best Sentence

Wait. Your teacher will tell you what to do.

1 O A cod is fish eating herring.
   O A tuna eats the cod.
   O A cat eats the can tuna.

6 O The sun really a big star.
   O It is a giant ball of light.
   O You hurt eyes if looking
      at the sun.

2 O Gardeners doesn't like
      weeds.
   O All weeds isn't bad.
   O People eat watercress and
      dandelion weeds.

7 O Fruits are good food.
   O Your body like fruits.
   O They taste good
      sometime.

3 O A kiwi is kind of fruit.
   O A kiwi is also a kind of
      bird.
   O A kiwi bird don't fly.

8 O Be carefully cross the
      street.
   O Stop and look for moving
      things like cars or trucks.
   O When it safe to cross,
      walk not run.

4 O Owls hid in tree holes
      in the daytime.
   O Most owls sleep during
      the day.
   O They go find food at night.

9 O All car have seat belt.
   O Seat belts save people
      riding in cars.
   O Always wearing a
      seatbelt when riding car.

5 O Two clouds are not the
      same.
   O Every cloud gots its name.
   O If it looks like thick cotton
      balls, I call it puffy.

10 O Do everybody read books?
   O We can learn much things
      from books.
   O Reading books can also
      be fun.

Are your answers right?

(Listen to your teacher.)

LESSON 24 – Reading a Map

In some tests you must find places in a map.

How Is The Test Given?   (Your teacher will tell you.)

Look at a test. What do you do in this test?

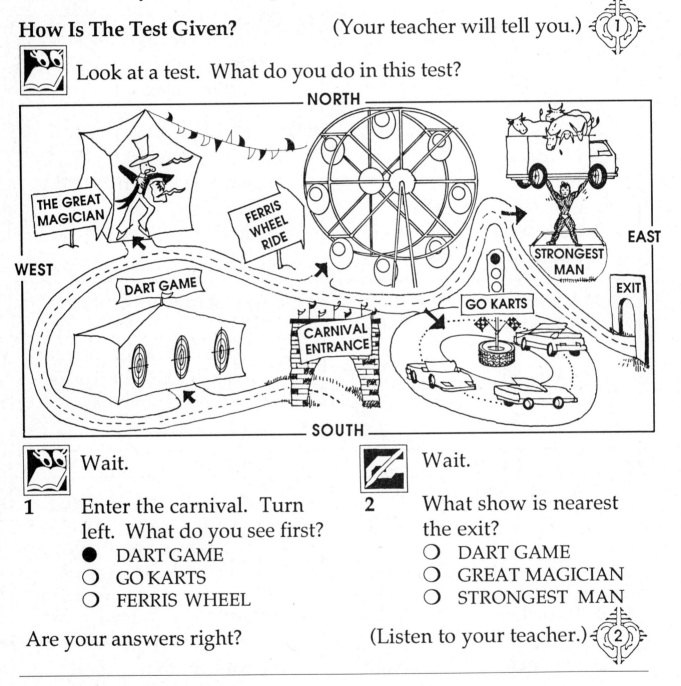

Wait.

Wait.

1   Enter the carnival. Turn left. What do you see first?
   - ● DART GAME
   - ○ GO KARTS
   - ○ FERRIS WHEEL

2   What show is nearest the exit?
   - ○ DART GAME
   - ○ GREAT MAGICIAN
   - ○ STRONGEST MAN

Are your answers right?   (Listen to your teacher.)

✔ **TEST HELP**
Remember:
- Look at the map very carefully.
- Read the question and the given answers carefully.
- Use your finger to help you find a place or direction on the map.

Find it on a map.

Your teacher will tell you what to do.

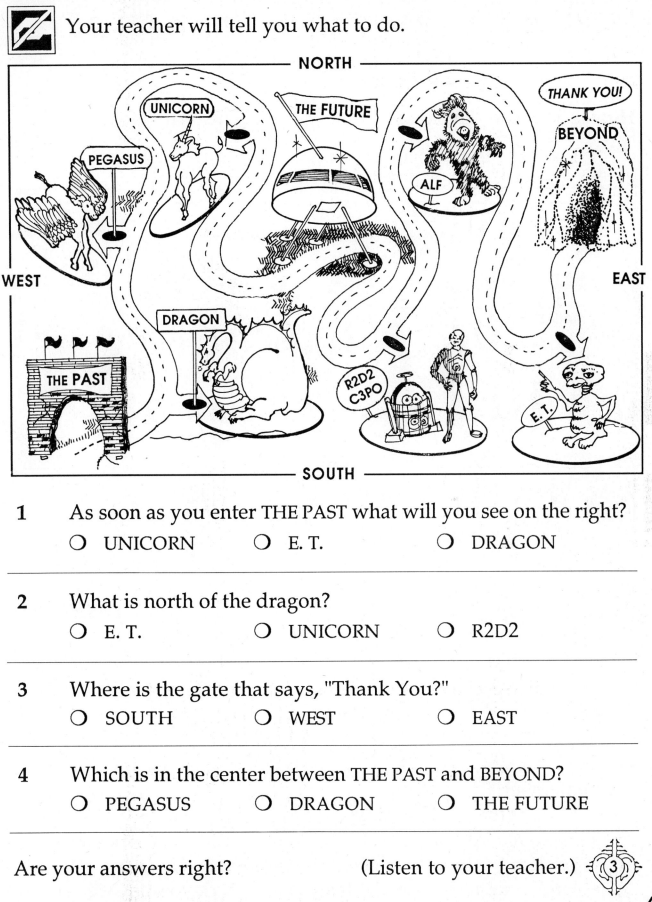

1. As soon as you enter THE PAST what will you see on the right?
   - ○ UNICORN
   - ○ E. T.
   - ○ DRAGON

2. What is north of the dragon?
   - ○ E. T.
   - ○ UNICORN
   - ○ R2D2

3. Where is the gate that says, "Thank You?"
   - ○ SOUTH
   - ○ WEST
   - ○ EAST

4. Which is in the center between THE PAST and BEYOND?
   - ○ PEGASUS
   - ○ DRAGON
   - ○ THE FUTURE

Are your answers right?   (Listen to your teacher.)

LESSON 25 – Reading a Street Map

Some tests ask about street maps.

How Is The Test Given?   (Your teacher will tell you.) ①

Look at a test. What do you do in this test?

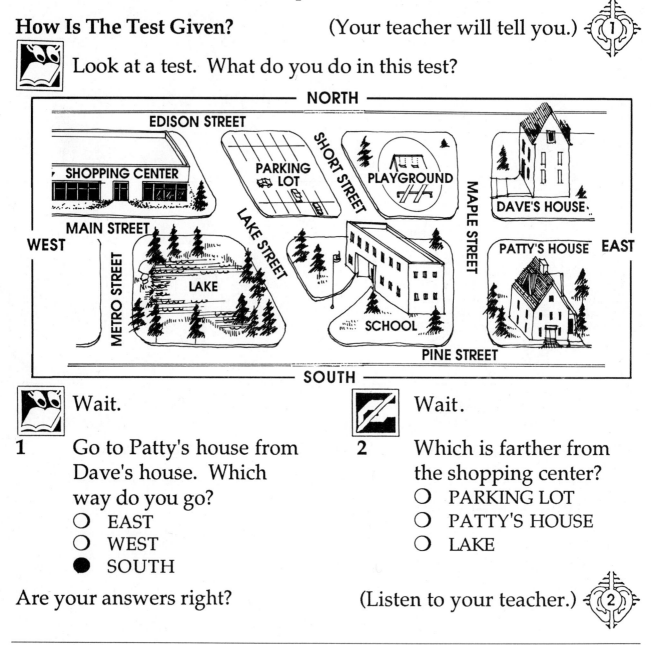

Wait.

1   Go to Patty's house from
         Dave's house. Which
         way do you go?
         ○ EAST
         ○ WEST
         ● SOUTH

Are your answers right?

Wait.

2   Which is farther from
         the shopping center?
         ○ PARKING LOT
         ○ PATTY'S HOUSE
         ○ LAKE

(Listen to your teacher.) ②

✔ **TEST HELP**
Remember:
• Look at the map. Look at everything on the map.
• Next, read the test question carefully. What is it asking for?
• Look at the given answers. Pick your answer.
• Find your answer on the map. Then mark your answer.

66

Find it on the street map.

Your teacher will tell you what to do.

---

1 On which street do you find the shopping center?

    ○ PINE ST.   ○ SHORT ST.   ○ MAIN ST.

---

2 You're in Dave's house. Where is the lake?

    ○ NORTH   ○ EAST   ○ WEST

---

3 From which street do you enter the school building?

    ○ METRO ST.   ○ EDISON ST.   ○ LAKE ST.

---

4 What is between the Lake and Patty's house?

    ○ SCHOOL   ○ PARKING LOT   ○ PLAYGROUND

---

5 What is just across Maple Street from Dave's house?

    ○ LAKE
    ○ PLAYGROUND
    ○ SHOPPING CENTER

---

6 A car leaves the Parking Lot. It goes south on Lake Street. Then it goes east on Pine Street. It stops on the corner of Pine and Maple Streets. Where is the car now?

    ○ PLAYGROUND
    ○ DAVE'S HOUSE
    ○ PATTY'S HOUSE

Are your answers right?   (Listen to your teacher.)

S LESSON 26 – Reading a Picture Graph

Some tests ask about a picture graph.

How Is The Test Given? (Your teacher will tell you.)

Look at a test. What do you do in this test?

YEAR BORN	NUMBER OF ELEPHANTS BORN IN ZOOS
1978	🐘 🐘 🐘 🐘
1981	🐘 🐘 🐘
1984	🐘
1987	🐘 🐘

How many elephants were born in 1981?

○ 1   ○ 2   ● 3

 Wait. Listen to your teacher.

In what year was the most number of elephants born in zoos?

○ 1978   ○ 1981   ○ 1984

Is your answer right?   (Listen to your teacher.)

✔ **TEST HELP**
Remember:
- Look at the picture graph carefully.
- Next, read the test question and the given answers.
- Look at the graph again. Then pick and mark your answer.

Find it in the graph.

FAVORITE PETS OF FIRST GRADERS	
Cat	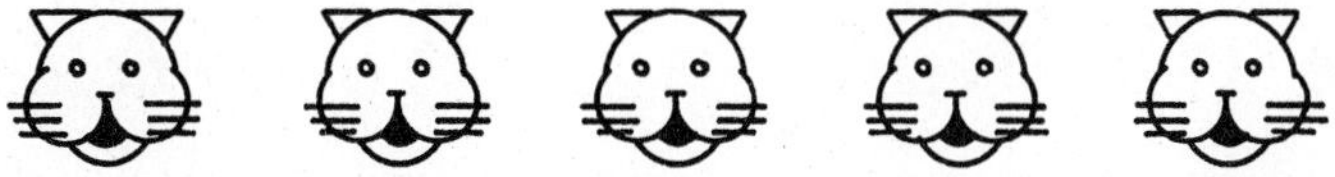 🐱 🐱 🐱 🐱 🐱
Dog	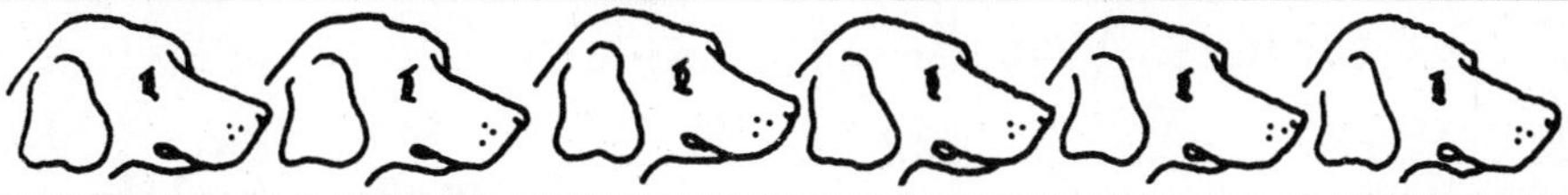 🐶 🐶 🐶 🐶 🐶 🐶
Hamster	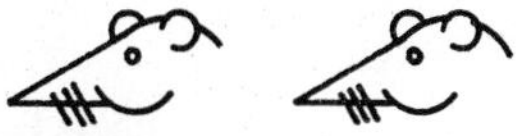 🐭 🐭
Chimp	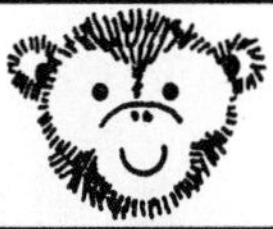 🐵
Frog	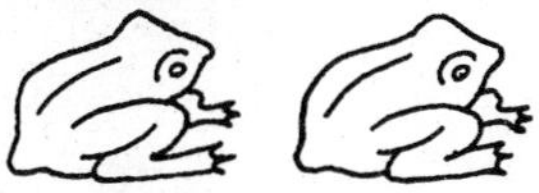 🐸 🐸

1   How many cats are pets of first graders?

    ○ 1   ○ 4   ○ 5

2   Which pet is the least favorite?

    ○ frog   ○ chimp   ○ dogs

3   Which two pets are even as favorites?

    ○ frog and cat   ○ dog and cat   ○ frog and hamster

4   Which kind of pet is the most favorite?

    ○ cat   ○ dog   ○ hamster

5   How many more students like dogs over cats?

    ○ 1   ○ 2   ○ 3

Are your answers right?   (Listen to your teacher.) ③

S LESSON 27 – Reading a Word Chart

Some tests ask questions about a word chart.

How Is The Test Given? (Your teacher will tell you.)

Look at a test. What do you do in this test?

CHERRY HILL'S WEATHER		
Sunday	rain	
Monday	sun	
Tuesday	rain	
Wednesday	sun	
Thursday	snow	
Friday	snow	
Saturday	rain	

Are your answers right?

Wait.

What was Wednesday's weather?

● sunny
○ rainy
○ snowy

 Wait.

Which two days had snow?

○ Sunday and Monday
○ Monday and Friday
○ Thursday and Friday

(Listen to your teacher.)

✔ **TEST HELP**

Remember:
• Look at the word chart carefully.
• Next, read the question and the given answers.
• Look at the chart again. Find the answer in the chart.
• Pick and mark your answer.

Find it in the Word Chart.

 Your teacher will tell you what to do.

THIS WEEK'S GAMES	
Sunday	baseball
Monday	soccer
Tuesday	basketball
Wednesday	no game
Thursday	tennis
Friday	soccer
Saturday	video game

1 What game will be played on Tuesday?

  ○ soccer
  ○ basketball
  ○ tennis

2 On which two days will there be the same game?

  ○ Monday and Friday
  ○ Sunday and Tuesday
  ○ Thursday and Friday

3 On which day is there no game?

  ○ Tuesday
  ○ Friday
  ○ Wednesday

4 How many days are there from no game to video game?

  ○ 1   ○ 2   ○ 4

Are your answers right?

(Listen to your teacher.) ⟨3⟩

S LESSON 28 – More Practice Tests

What Have You Learned in Lessons 24 to 27?

Read a Map

Your teacher will tell you what to do.

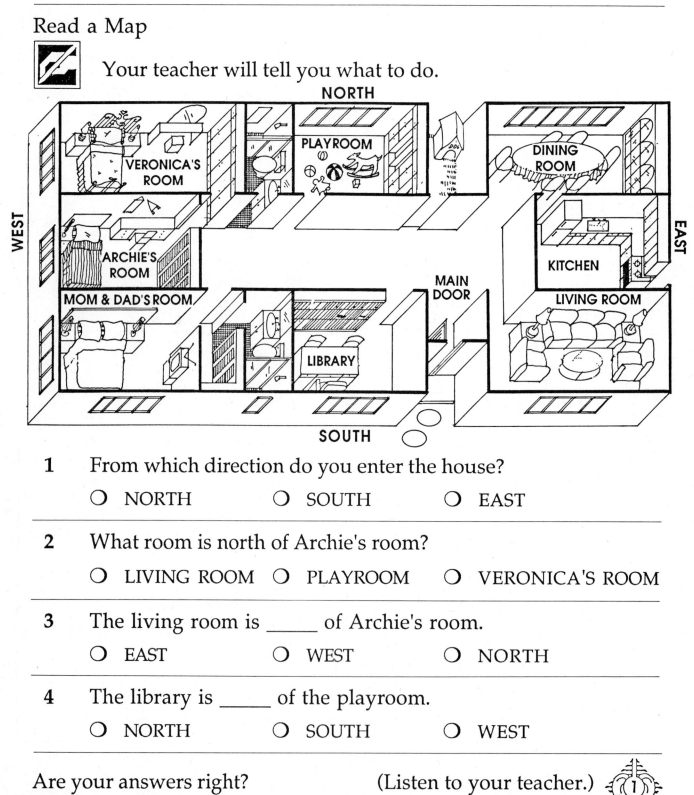

1 From which direction do you enter the house?

○ NORTH   ○ SOUTH   ○ EAST

2 What room is north of Archie's room?

○ LIVING ROOM   ○ PLAYROOM   ○ VERONICA'S ROOM

3 The living room is _____ of Archie's room.

○ EAST   ○ WEST   ○ NORTH

4 The library is _____ of the playroom.

○ NORTH   ○ SOUTH   ○ WEST

Are your answers right?   (Listen to your teacher.)

More Practice ....

Read a Picture Graph

 Your teacher will tell you what to do.

VITO'S GARDEN	
Trees	
Shrubs	
Flower Plants	

1 How many trees are there in Vito's garden?

    ○ 5   ○ 8   ○ 7

2 How many more shrubs than trees are there in Vito's garden?

    ○ 1   ○ 2   ○ 3

3 Which is the largest group of plants in his garden?

    ○ trees   ○ shrubs   ○ flower plants

4 How many more flower plants and trees are there than shrubs?

    ○ 2   ○ 3   ○ 4

Are your answers right?   (Listen to your teacher.)

Read a Word Chart

 Your teacher will tell you what to do.

HOW MANY DAYS IN DECEMBER?	
Rainy days	5
Sunny days	11
Cloudy days	7
Snowy days	8

1 How many days did the sun shine in December?

- ○ 5
- ○ 8
- ○ 11

3 Which happened the fewest number of days?

- ○ It snowed.
- ○ It rained.
- ○ The sun shone.

2 How many more sunny days were there than rainy days?

- ○ 6
- ○ 7
- ○ 8

4 How many days are there in December?

- ○ 25
- ○ 30
- ○ 31

Are your answers right?

(Listen to your teacher.)

More Practice ....

Read a Word Chart

Your teacher will tell you what to do.

PAT'S CHORES LAST WEEK	
SUNDAY	watered garden plants
MONDAY	threw the trash
TUESDAY	helped cook supper
WEDNESDAY	cleaned room
THURSDAY	washed the dog
FRIDAY	helped wash dishes
SATURDAY	helped wash clothes

1 What did Pat do on Thursday?
- ○ washed the dog
- ○ cleaned room
- ○ watered plants

2 On what day was Pat in the garden?
- ○ Sunday
- ○ Tuesday
- ○ Friday

3 On which two days was Pat in the kitchen?
- ○ Sunday and Monday
- ○ Tuesday and Friday
- ○ Thursday and Friday

Are your answers right?

(Listen to your teacher.)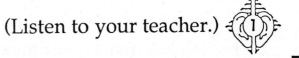

75

LESSON 29 – Putting Words in A-B-C Order

Some tests ask you to put pictures and words in **a-b-c** order.

How Is The Test Given?

happy

family

toy

kitten

Are your answers right?

(Your teacher will tell you.)

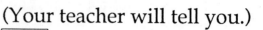 Wait. Listen.

1   Which picture should come right before the picture of the toy?
   ● kitten
   ○ family
   ○ happy

 Wait. Listen.

2   On which page will you put the picture of the family?
   ○ first
   ○ last
   ○ second

3   What picture should be on the last page of the test dictionary?
   ○ happy
   ○ toy
   ○ kitten

(Listen to your teacher.)

✔ **TEST HELP**
Remember:
- Look at each picture dictionary page.
  Look at the first letter of each picture's name.
  See how the first letters would be put in **a-b-c** order.
- Read the test question and the test answers.
- Look at the test dictionary again.
- Pick and mark your answer.

Put pictures and words in A-B-C order.

Your teacher will tell you what to do.

1   Which picture comes right after the picture of the apple?

   ○ rope   ○ glass   ○ clown

2   Which picture comes right before the picture of a glass?

   ○ clown   ○ eye   ○ horse

3   Which picture comes between the picture of the horse and the picture of the tiger?

   ○ watch   ○ clown   ○ rope

Are your answers right?   (Listen to your teacher.)

S LESSON 30 – Using a Dictionary

Some tests ask questions about dictionary words and meanings.

How Is The Test Given?   (Your teacher will tell you.) ①

Look at a test. What do you do in this test?

Wait. Listen to your teacher.

dentist
a person who
takes care of
your teeth

hurt
to make
somebody
feel bad

nurse
a person who
takes care of
sick people

sick
when you're
not well

How do you spell the name of a person who takes care of
sick people?

○ ners   ○ nurs   ● nurse

Wait. Listen to your teacher.

Which of these words tell you that you made a person feel bad?

○ dentist   ○ hurt   ○ sick

Is your answer right?   (Listen to your teacher.) ②

✔ **TEST HELP**
Remember:
- Read the test dictionary words and meanings.
- Listen carefully to the test question.
  Read the given answers carefully.
- Look at the test dictionary words and meanings again.
  Pick and mark your answer.

Find it in the Dictionary.

Your teacher will tell you what to do.

alligator
an animal that lives in water

apple
a type of fruit

ax
a tool used to chop wood

zebra
an animal with stripes on its body

zero
none, or nothing

zoo
a place where many different animals live

1   How do you spell the name of an animal with stripes on its body?

   ○ alligator   ○ zebra   ○ zero

2   Where can you find many different kinds of animals?

   ○ zoo   ○ zero   ○ zebra

3   Which word is the name of something you can eat?

   ○ apple   ○ ax   ○ alligator

4   Which word names a number that is lower than one?

   ○ zoo   ○ zero   ○ ax

5   Which word spells the name of an animal that lives in water and walks on land?

   ○ alligator   ○ aligator   ○ alligater

Are your answers right?   (Listen to your teacher.)

LESSON 31 – Using the Table of Contents

A Table of Contents is a part of a book.
It shows the things you can read about in the book.
Some tests ask about a book's table of contents.

How Is The Test Given? (Your teacher will tell you.)

Look at a test. What do you do in this test?

```
TABLE OF CONTENTS
                          Page
Sun    .......................   3
Moon   .......................  17
Stars  .......................  31
```

1   Which page might tell you how you can get a tan or a dark skin?

    ○ 31   ● 3   ○ 17

Wait. Listen to your teacher.

2   Which pages would tell about moonlight?

    ○ 3 to 16   ○ 31 to 40   ○ 17 to 30

3   Which of these bright things will you read about on page 31?

    ○ sun   ○ moon   ○ stars

Are your answers right? (Listen to your teacher.)

✔ **TEST HELP**
Remember:
- Read the table of contents carefully. Look at the page where you begin to read about each thing in the book.
- Look for clue words in the test question.
- Use your finger to find the answer in the table of contents. Then mark the circle for your answer.

Use a Table of Contents.

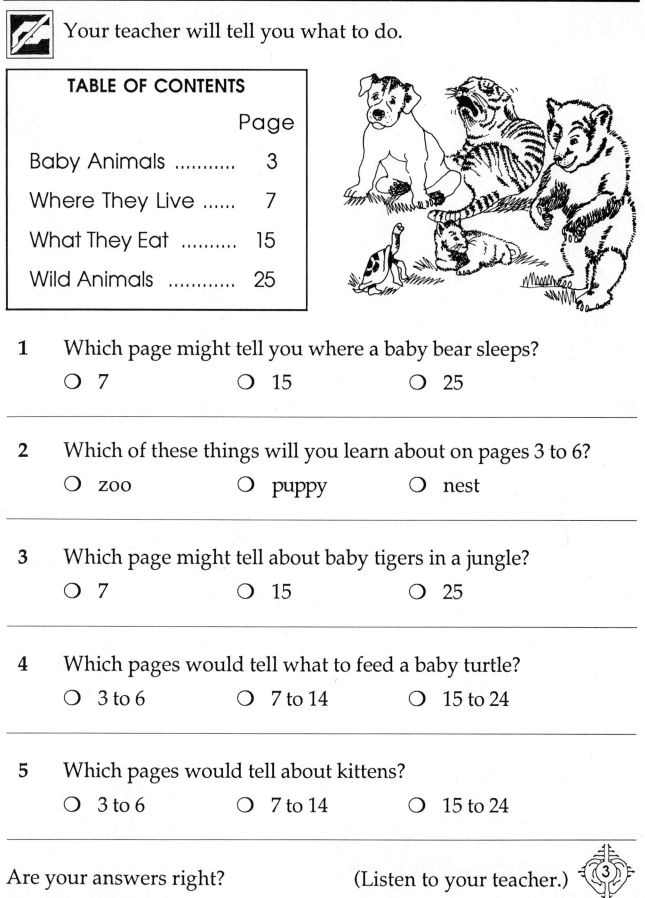

Your teacher will tell you what to do.

1 Which page might tell you where a baby bear sleeps?

○ 7   ○ 15   ○ 25

2 Which of these things will you learn about on pages 3 to 6?

○ zoo   ○ puppy   ○ nest

3 Which page might tell about baby tigers in a jungle?

○ 7   ○ 15   ○ 25

4 Which pages would tell what to feed a baby turtle?

○ 3 to 6   ○ 7 to 14   ○ 15 to 24

5 Which pages would tell about kittens?

○ 3 to 6   ○ 7 to 14   ○ 15 to 24

Are your answers right?   (Listen to your teacher.)

LESSON 32 – Knowing Where to Look

A test may ask where you can find some useful facts.

How Is The Test Given?   (Your teacher will tell you.)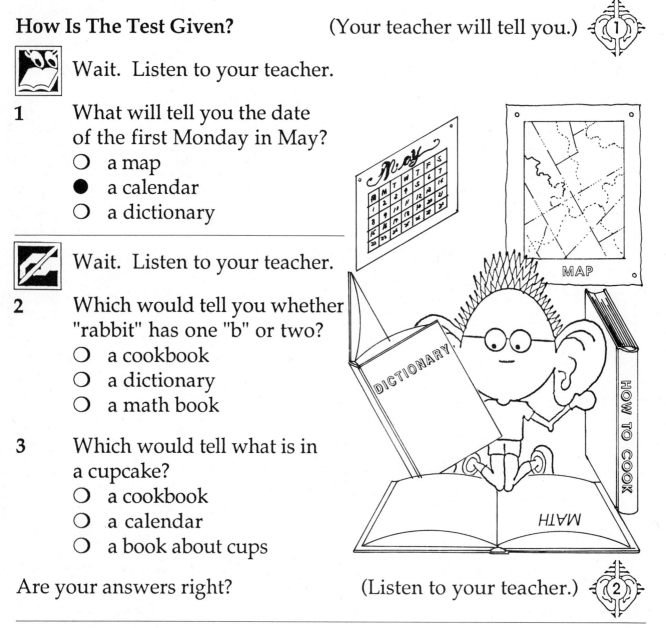

Wait. Listen to your teacher.

1   What will tell you the date
of the first Monday in May?
  ○ a map
  ● a calendar
  ○ a dictionary

Wait. Listen to your teacher.

2   Which would tell you whether
"rabbit" has one "b" or two?
  ○ a cookbook
  ○ a dictionary
  ○ a math book

3   Which would tell what is in
a cupcake?
  ○ a cookbook
  ○ a calendar
  ○ a book about cups

Are your answers right?   (Listen to your teacher.)

✔ **TEST HELP**
Remember:
  • Read the test question carefully. What useful fact is needed?
    Where can you find this fact?
  • Then look at the test answers.
    Pick and mark your answer.

Where can you find these useful facts?

Your teacher will tell you what to do.

1   Which will tell you on what day
    June 5 will be this year?
    ○   a math book
    ○   a calendar
    ○   a dictionary

2   Which will tell the page where
    you can read about something?
    ○   a table of contents
    ○   a dictionary
    ○   a book about something

3   Which might tell the price of
    a new car?
    ○   a reading book
    ○   a telephone book
    ○   a newspaper ad

4   Which book would tell what
    the word "casserole" means?
    ○   a telephone book
    ○   a dictionary
    ○   a book about castles

5   Which of these will tell you the
    number to call to get the police?
    ○   a telephone book
    ○   a dictionary
    ○   a book about cops

Are your answers right?   (Listen to your teacher.)

LESSON 33 – More Practice Tests

What Have You Learned in Lessons 29 to 32?

Put Words in A-B-C Order

Wait. Your teacher will tell you what to do.

cow

tree

woman

ax

plow

house

---

1 Which picture comes between those of the plow and a woman?

   ○ tree   ○ house   ○ a x

---

2 Which picture must be right before the picture of a house?

   ○ woman   ○ plow   ○ cow

---

3 Look at the picture dictionary page at the right.

Where will you place it in the picture dictionary?

   ○ right before the picture of a plow
   ○ between the pictures of the plow and the tree
   ○ right after the picture of a tree

rabbit

Are your answers right?   (Listen to your teacher.)

Use a Dictionary

Your teacher will tell you what to do.

hurl
 to throw

leopard
 a meat-eating wild
 animal with dark spots
 on its yellow skin

rescue
 to save from being
 hurt or destroyed

shaggy
 has long rough hair

sly
 clever and tricky

stumble
 to fall or trip over
 something

1 Which of these spells the name of an animal with dark spots
 on yellow skin?
 ○ leopard ○ loepard ○ lepard

2 Which word means the same as "hurl?"
 ○ rescue ○ throw ○ fall

3 Which word might show what someone's hair looks like?
 ○ stumble ○ sly ○ shaggy

4 Which word is often used when talking about a fox?
 ○ rescue ○ hurl ○ sly

5 Which word tells what may happen if you run down the stairs?
 ○ hurl ○ stumble ○ shaggy

Are your answers right? (Listen to your teacher.)

More Practice ....

Use a Table of Contents

Your teacher will tell you what to do.

1 Which page will tell you about dogs?

○ 17   ○ 29   ○ 3

---

2 On what page will the book start to tell about birds?

○ 1   ○ 17   ○ 3

---

3 Which pages will tell about goldfish?

○ 3 to 16   ○ 17 to 28   ○ 29 to 40

---

4 Under which name will you look to find out about eagles?

○ Birds   ○ Fishes   ○ Animals

Are your answers right?   (Listen to your teacher.)

Know Where to Look for Useful Facts

Your teacher will tell you what to do

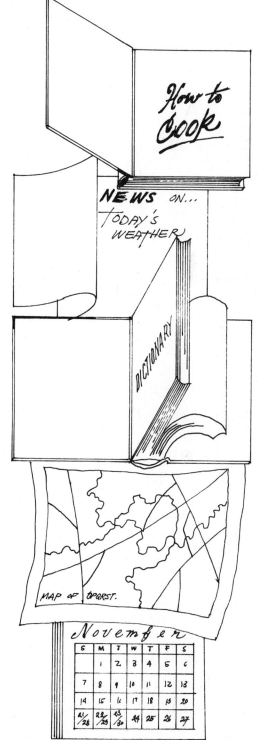

1 Which will tell you what date Thanksgiving will be this year?

- ○ a dictionary
- ○ a calendar
- ○ a map

2 Which will tell you where the shopping center is located in a town?

- ○ a map
- ○ a calendar
- ○ a cookbook

3 Which will tell you if the word "butterfly" has one "t" or two?

- ○ a dictionary
- ○ a newspaper
- ○ a calendar

4 Where might you read about today's weather?

- ○ a dictionary
- ○ a newspaper
- ○ a calendar

Are your answers right?

(Listen to your teacher.)

A
LESSON 34 – Questions About Numbers

This test will show how much you know about numbers.

How Is The Test Given?   (Your teacher will tell you.)

Look at a test. What do you do in this test?

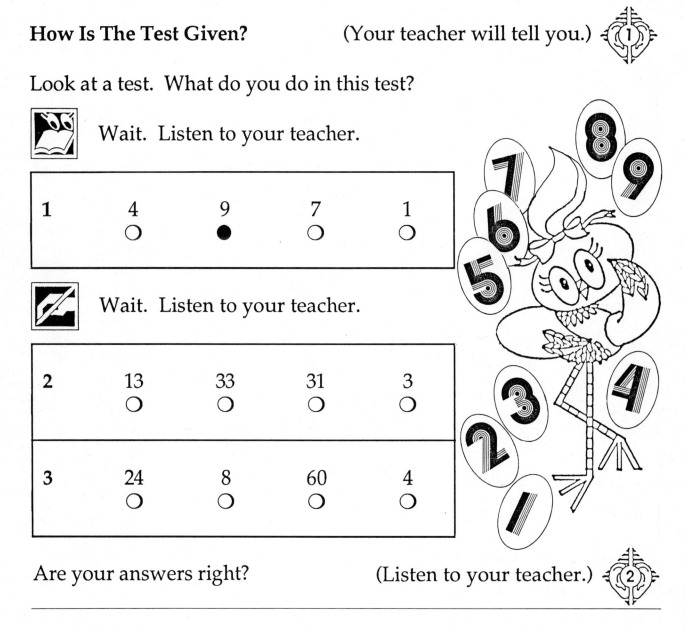

Wait. Listen to your teacher.

1	4	9	7	1
	○	●	○	○

Wait. Listen to your teacher.

2	13	33	31	3
	○	○	○	○

3	24	8	60	4
	○	○	○	○

Are your answers right?   (Listen to your teacher.)

✔ **TEST HELP**
Remember:
- Listen carefully to the test question.
- Then look at the given test answers.
  Which is the correct answer?
- Pick and mark the circle below your answer.

Try these tests.

Your teacher will tell you what to do.

1 Mark the circle below the number seventeen.

| 77 | 7 | 17 | 71 |
| ○ | ○ | ○ | ○ |

2 Which number is forty-one?

| 14 | 41 | 40 | 4 |
| ○ | ○ | ○ | ○ |

3 Which number is one more than 26?

| 24 | 25 | 27 | 37 |
| ○ | ○ | ○ | ○ |

4 What number will you get if you add 6 and 7?

| 14 | 40 | 13 | 12 |
| ○ | ○ | ○ | ○ |

5 Which number is closest to 5?

| 6 | 2 | 8 | 9 |
| ○ | ○ | ○ | ○ |

6 How many numbers are there between 20 and 40?

| 10 | 19 | 25 | 30 |
| ○ | ○ | ○ | ○ |

7 Which shape has only 4 boxes in it?

8 How much money is there in all?

| 25 ¢ | 30 ¢ | 31 ¢ | 35 ¢ |
| ○ | ○ | ○ | ○ |

Are your answers right?

(Listen to your teacher.)

A LESSON 35 – Working With Word Problems

On some tests, you will listen to, or read word problems.
Then you will add or subtract to find the answer to the problem.

How Is The Test Given?   (Your teacher will tell you.)

Look at a test. What do you do in this test?

1	1	2	3	NH
	○	●	○	○

Wait. Listen to your teacher.

2	2	3	5	NH
	○	○	○	○

3	20 ¢	25 ¢	35 ¢	NH
	○	○	○	○

Are your answers right?   (Listen to your teacher.)

✔ **TEST HELP**
Remember:
- Listen carefully to the word problem.
  What is the problem about? Will you add or subtract?
- Add or subtract in your mind.
  Or, do the work on a piece of paper.
- Next, look at the given test answers. If your answer is among them, mark the circle beside it. If the answer is not given, mark the circle below NH, for Not Here.

Try these tests.

Your teacher will tell you what to do.

1 (Listen.)

2   3   4   NH
○   ○   ○   ○

2 (Listen.)

5   6   7   NH
○   ○   ○   ○

3 (Listen.)

55 c   65 c   75 c   NH
○   ○   ○   ○

4 (Listen.)

1   2   3   NH
○   ○   ○   ○

5 (Listen.)

5   10   15   NH
○   ○   ○   ○

6 (Listen.)

Tom owns a parrot.
Jerry owns an eagle.
How many birds do they
have in all?

1   2   3   NH
○   ○   ○   ○

7 (Listen.)
Cindy had 5 dogs.
She gave 2 dogs to Mark.
How many dogs are left
with Cindy?

1   2   3   NH
○   ○   ○   ○

8 (Listen.)
Laurie bought 2 pencils.
One pencil cost 10 cents.
The other pencil cost 5 cents.
How much did the pencils cost?

5 ¢   10 ¢   15 ¢   NH
○   ○   ○   ○

Are your answers right?

(Listen to your teacher.)

A LESSON 36 – Working With Numbers

Some tests give number problems.

How Is The Test Given? (Your teacher will tell you.)

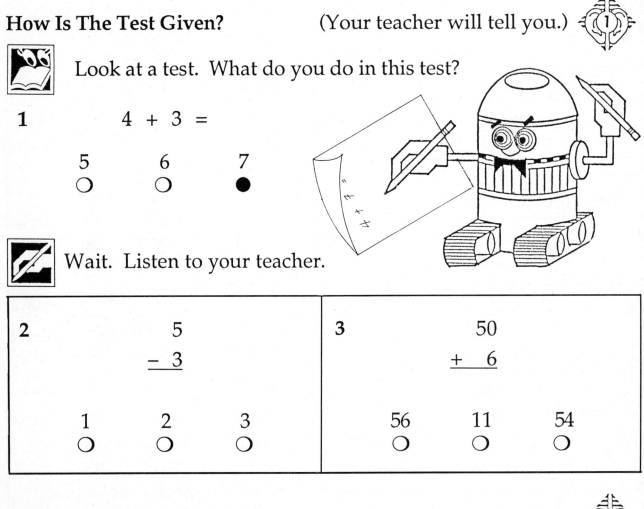

Look at a test. What do you do in this test?

1   4 + 3 =

   5   6   7
   ○   ○   ●

Wait. Listen to your teacher.

2 5 – 3	3 50 + 6
1 2 3 ○ ○ ○	56 11 54 ○ ○ ○

Are your answers right?   (Listen to your teacher.)

✔ **TEST HELP**
Remember:
- Look closely at the number problem.
  Are you asked to add or to subtract?
- Add or subtract in your mind.
  Or, do the work on a piece of paper.
- Then look at the given answers.
- Pick and mark your answer.

Try these tests.

Your teacher will tell you what to do.

1   2 + 3 =

| 7 | 5 | 6 | NH |
| ○ | ○ | ○ | ○ |

2   5 − 1 =

| 2 | 4 | 6 | NH |
| ○ | ○ | ○ | ○ |

3   7 − 2 =

| 4 | 5 | 6 | NH |
| ○ | ○ | ○ | ○ |

4   3 + 1 + 2 =

| 4 | 5 | 6 | NH |
| ○ | ○ | ○ | ○ |

5   10 + 6 + 1 =

| 16 | 17 | 18 | NH |
| ○ | ○ | ○ | ○ |

6   20 + 8 =

| 18 | 28 | 38 | NH |
| ○ | ○ | ○ | ○ |

7
$$\begin{array}{r} 12 \\ -\ 10 \end{array}$$

| 1 | 2 | 3 | NH |
| ○ | ○ | ○ | ○ |

8
$$\begin{array}{r} 30 \\ +\ 20 \end{array}$$

| 40 | 60 | 70 | NH |
| ○ | ○ | ○ | ○ |

9
$$\begin{array}{r} 29 \\ -\ 11 \end{array}$$

| 18 | 19 | 20 | NH |
| ○ | ○ | ○ | ○ |

10
$$\begin{array}{r} 25 \\ -\ 10 \end{array}$$

| 10 | 15 | 5 | NH |
| ○ | ○ | ○ | ○ |

Are your answers right?   (Listen to your teacher.)   3

A LESSON 37 – More Practice Tests

What Have You Learned in Lessons 34 to 36?

Work With Numbers

 Wait. Listen to your teacher.

1	(Listen.)				**5**		$25 - 13 =$		
	78 ○	87 ○	86 ○	68 ○		12 ○	14 ○	16 ○	NH ○
2	(Listen.)				**6**		$\begin{array}{r} 20 \\ + \ 2 \\ \hline \end{array}$		
	97 ○	79 ○	89 ○	98 ○		18 ○	20 ○	22 ○	NH ○
3	(Listen.)				**7**		$\begin{array}{r} 19 \\ - \ 12 \\ \hline \end{array}$		
	7 ○	10 ○	15 ○	22 ○		5 ○	7 ○	10 ○	NH ○
4	(Listen.)				**8**				
	10 ○	20 ○	30 ○	35 ○		○	○	○	

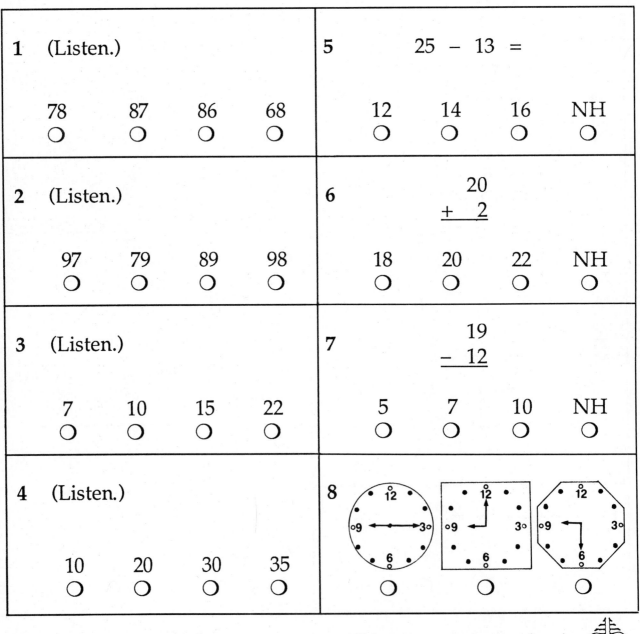

Are your answers right?   (Listen to your teacher.)

94

More Practice ....

Work With Word Problems

 Wait. Your teacher will tell you what to do.

1   George put 3 apples in the basket.
    Mary put 2 more apples.
    How many apples are now in the basket?

    ○ 5   ○ 8   ○ 10   ○ NH

2   Al had 7 oranges.
    He gave 2 of them to Karen.
    How many oranges were left with Al?

    ○ 3   ○ 4   ○ 5   ○ NH

3   Tom bought 10 oranges.
    Jerry bought 10 more.
    How many oranges did they buy in all?

    ○ 10   ○ 15   ○ 20   ○ NH

4   John is 3 feet and 9 inches tall.
    Jack is 3 feet and 4 inches tall.
    How many inches taller is John than Jack?

    ○ 6   ○ 7   ○ 8   ○ NH

5   Jim had 15 pieces of candy. He ate some.
    Now, he has only 5 pieces of candy left.
    How many pieces of candy did he eat?

    ○ 6   ○ 8   ○ 9   ○ NH

Are your answers right?   (Listen to your teacher.) 1

Your test taking friends –
    eye popping BIG EYES,
    beeping HAN 'CIL,
    and jumping BIG EARS

    are so happy for you.